D0271025

HO! HO! HO!
Ho! Ho! Ho!
Ho Ho Ho!
BUNTIN
SALE DEC 29
BABES in the WOOD
PRIVATE
BABES in the WOOD
TOWN HALL
ton Borough wishes you all a very
HAPPY CHRISTMAS!
BUS STOP
Shuddup!
It's NOT FUNNY!

Good King Wenceslas looked out, on the Feast of Stephen....
When the snow lay round about, deep and crisp and even:
Who's that bloke?
Where & what his dwelling?
Sire, he lives a good league hence,
In the inner city....
Struggling by on fifty pence,
Deserving all your pity!
Poor Soul! Better have a whip round
Take this sovereign and this tie..
This clever bar utensil...
And this stilton and this pie...
This matching pen & pencil!
Thanks, guv!
Always give to those in need...
Mark my kindly action!
When you GIVE, then you RECEIVE
Lasting satisfaction!
Hear Hear!
Brightly shone the guests that night, for their hearts were merry....
Tucking in and getting tight, on Crème de Menthe and sherry!
I say, what is 6 inches long, with hair one end and a hole the other?
A tooth brush! HAA HAA Haaa!!
WAH Haaa!! Haa Haa!!!

Pure Posy

also by Posy Simmonds

MRS WEBER'S DIARY
TRUE LOVE
PICK OF POSY
VERY POSY
FRED

Pure Posy

POSY SIMMONDS

Methuen

for Richard

First published by Jonathan Cape Ltd in 1987
This edition published in 1989 by Methuen London
81, Fulham Road, London SW3 6RB

ISBN: 0 413 62530 3

A CIP catalogue record for this book
is available from the British Library

The drawings in this book have been taken from episodes of the weekly cartoon strip appearing in the *Guardian*, from *Harper's Magazine*, New York and from the *Sunday Times*

Printed in Great Britain by
St Edmundsbury Press Ltd, Bury St Edmunds, Suffolk

Good King Wenceslas popped out.....
Brightly shone the moon that night
Tho' the frost was cruel.....
Four million poor men came in sight
Gathering winter fuel.....
Great Scott!
Another Whip-round!
A Whipround! You must be jesting!!
And heated were these lucky sods
And their manner chilly...
What! Shell out four million sovs?
..Don't be bloody silly!!
Lock and bar thy fortress door
If thou know'st it telling!
Yonder Peasantry is sore...
Hearken what they're yelling!
Ingrates!
JOBS!
Bread!
Don't bore us with your talk of strikes.....
Or your whingeing blether!
Off your bums and on your bikes!.....
And pull yourselves TOGETHER!

Forbidden Fruit

Susie..it's been a long time...
Not..
..So long

Trouble is...whenever I see you... ...I think of one thing...
Still?
Yes...still...

And you?...I suppose it's... different for you...you're over it... You don't still feel..?
Over it!? How can you say that!?

Soon as I SAW you, I thought: Oh God! Oh God! How can I stay away from you tonight...?
...You're the only man I know, who......

Then, you still...?
Yes..Stanhope I'm not over it... I never will be! SIGH
Darling!

In that case.. ...shall we?
What?

...You know...for old time's sake
Stanhope! NO!

I'm sorry!
I MUST!
I can't help it!
What! HERE!!?
You're MAD! They'll see us!

Close the door... no one'll see...
Stanhope! What're you DOING!!? I can't! ...I can't..you're CRAZY!

Yes you can... Just for me...
But John'll find out! He will..he always knows when I have...
I'm so bad at hiding it...
And what about Trish? We PROMISED, Stanhope... We DID! We SWORE we'd never do it again!

But you want to... don't you...eh?
Course I bloody do! Soon as I saw you, I wanted to....

Come on! Out here!
Quick one out here... come on...
Oh no.. ...oh...

Oh! I'm trembling! Oh, we'll feel so terrible after! Oh! What the hell!

Oh, darling..it's been so long!
Quick!
Gimme it!
Hang on...

There...just the one...
Oh
Oh!
Oh!

Oh Stanhope...God, this is wonderful! Aaaaah! Mmmm
Oh bliss! Aaaah!

Good Samaritans
HLLB!

It is a dark winter's night in the inner city:
Hic!
Yuuerh!
Hic!
Gawd!

Here is a poor, legless man, in great need...
Yuuhr.. feel like a vulture's jock-strap!
GLLB!

...Here are *certain* others, who look on him.....
HULC
BLB!

...and pass by on the other side...
Disgusting old lush!

Hlp!
Bulp!

Allo!
ULFF!

Bleedin' nuffin' in iss one....

In 'is jackit...
QUICK!
Blp!

Oni twenny notes...
Wewull, at's no bleedin' use!

Give 'im a Li'oll Noo Year Present, Shall we?
Yeh!

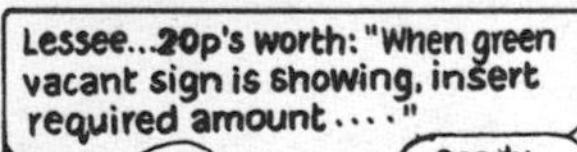
Lessee...20p's worth: "When green vacant sign is showing, insert required amount...."

QUICK!
Bulp!
Ready... Erewego!

'Ere you go, guv! 'Ave iss one on us!
Blup!

toilet
Oright in 'ere, guv?
toilet

'Ere's yer twenny notes
Never better! I'm feeling in SHOW-ROOM condition now....
Oright, now, guv?
Show-room condition!

What year did you say we're in now?
Tiger...it's the Chinese Year of the Tiger...
Ah...Tiger.
...And, last year... what was that?
Ox, wasn't it, Lizzie? Year of the Ox?
Yes, 1985 was OX... ...bloody terrible year it was too!
Yes! Absolute PITS!
A real bastard!
God awful year!
Famines.... ...volcanoes... ...plane crashes..
That terrible earthquake.... ...terrible!
As for here! Bad to God-Awful!
Yes...what with miners ...the riots... another million on the dole...
The desperation people must feel! You feel so sorry... ..so helpless.... ..just TERRIBLE!
..the social inequalities
The social degeneracy
Oh Gawd! Here they go again!
Bleeding Hearts Club!
And you can't really blame people for behaving badly...I know I would if I was unemployed for years.....
Sue & me are unemployed, Dad...
Oh, I don't count you, Adrian..not as if you do anything about it except lounge around here, watching TV....
I just think 1985 was IMPOVERISHING in every way.... ..economically...
Yes!
..spiritually..
..culturally..
..morally!
God it was!
Yes...a really horrible year... so depressing... the awful drift into gregarities!
GRIM beyond belief!
I just don't know how we all survived it!
They've never had it so bad....
But 1985 sounds like being a terrific wine year!
So they say... ...may turn out as good as '81!
Champagne looks good ...very small vintage in '85... but it's supposed to be a glorious year!
Oh GOODY!
Oh wonderful
Yes, particularly the Bordeaux!
Snarl!
Snarl!
1986. The Year of the Tiger:
n Ltd. Wine Merchar
Snarl!
Snarl!

Sandra.. if I said to you: someink LOOKED like a duck...n' WALKED like a duck...n' QUACKED like a duck...what would you call it?
DUCK, of course! Stands to reason...

Right...
..and if I'd said to you, five years ago... about this middle-class lot, here...'oo took this street over....
Cuckoo, Pippa!

...if I'd said: They look like NOBS......
****! My nail!
Careful with the claret, darling

...and they LIVE like NOBS....
Oh yeah! All extensions and bidets..& utility rooms ...& au pairs & dinner parties....

..and they SOUND like NOBS....
Oh, super, Gemma! See you both Saturday, sort of 8 for 8·30ish?
Super!

....but they don't THINK like NOBS.....
At least if they invested in the infrastructure, something would be done about unemployment!
Quite!

And where's all the North Sea money going?!
Not into the Health Service, that's for sure!

NOT using the money from mortgage-interest tax relief... NOT putting that money directly into housing, is CRIMINAL!
If you can't rent & can't pay off a £25,000 mortgage where the hell are people expected to live !!?

I dunno HOW people can send their kids to PRIVATE schools!

...you'd've called 'em?
Sort of middle-class Socialists....
Right!

Yeah..well.. my problem is... what d'you call this particular lot here, nowadays?.......

...cos they still LOOK like ducks..........
Got a lot of elbow, this Brouilly, Leo!

....but now they QUACKS like ducks!
See, you've got to be REALISTIC... we've got to learn to live with a degree of unemployment....
You can't just legislate it away!
True
mm

..the local comprehensive's SO DIRE! I feel FRIGHTFUL, but really, we've no option BUT to send him privately..... what does one DO!...
Oh I know!

...and they LIVE like ducks.....
Couldn't these go to the cottage, darling?
They're so 60's!
cos I've seen the most perfect C.19 silk moiré at Rutland Antiques!

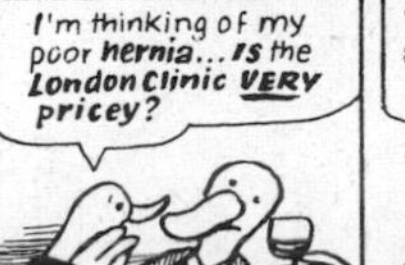
I'm thinking of my poor hernia... IS the London Clinic VERY pricey?

This house? Well...it should fetch £190,000 if we're lucky...

And how're our T.S.B. shares doing today?

Tsk..Lor Love-a-duck...

The Ratings

..I tell you, Gloria... that child's not MINE!...WHOSE is it?! Come on, who's the father?

It's YOURS! I keep telling you!
You lying..!

It's Slater's, isn't it? It's his bastard...!
No! No!

I Don't!
You bloody DO!
If I...get my hands on that little chickenshi
...!!
No, Barry, NO!

Look, if you want to lead a totally selfish life, go and do it elsewhere!
Outta my way, you
!
AAGH! Barreee! NO!!

Meaning WHAT?
I don't know ...I'm just... SICK of you!
BUNTING's BIG Winter SALE ON NOW!

You treat me like a servant! You're OUT every NIGHT!.... You leave ME to do EVERYTHING!
... just plain country FITNESS... ...without the FATNESS.... ...and all the TASTE of BUTTER.....

Not EVERY night... I was in at the weekend.. well, I was on Sunday...
YAWN
...more absorbent... ...stronger...... SOFTEST ever....

Ooh, Dave thank God you're here!
Barry! If you lay ONE finger on Gloria, I'm going to RAM your teeth down your ASS..so help me!

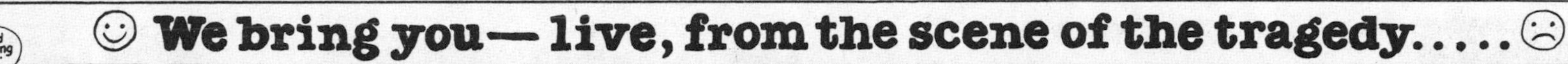
We bring you — live, from the scene of the tragedy.....

Good evening

...And now, back to Jon Pollit, live, from the scene of the tragedy...
NEWS

... No further casualties... ...but any minute now...

...more of the relatives of the dead & injured, who witnessed this terrible tragedy, will be leaving the building, . . .

Ah...Excuse me...Mrs Baker is it?... Mrs Baker, excuse me...

...this must be a very distressing time for you...could you say something about your feelings at this mo...

It must've been a terrible shock... Could you say how you feel, after...?

...Mrs Baker, ...could you?
Mrs Baker...

You, sir, how do you..?
Sir?
Sir?
How do I feel?

Oarf!
That's how I feel!

Can we have a close-up on this?
Uaff!
UFF!

Oof!
Mr Pollit?
Jon?
This must be a very distressing moment for you...

...Can you describe your feelings at this moment in time?... Mr Pollit?
Jon?
Uff!

..And now, the baby rhino who met a Princess...

And that's it....

Have a nice day!

No.56: Little Ones' Lunch

This week, *busy* mature student & mother-of-six, *Wendy Weber*, guides you through the favourite eating experience of her Under Sevens.....

Menu

Fizzy Drink

Noodles with Sauce

Stew, Mash, Peas

Jelly 'n' ice cream

Chocolate Digestive Biscuit

Wendy and husband, *George*, believe in feeding the younger members of their lively brood, SIMPLE, *balanced* meals.....

Fizzy Drink:

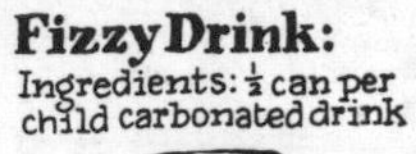

Ingredients: ½ can per child carbonated drink

Noodles with Sauce:

Stew, Mash, Peas:

Jelly 'n' ice cream:

Chocolate Digestive Biscuits:

3. Lick off all the chocolate....

MEN'S TALK

Tamsin
Ha ha haa Hee ha ha hee hee!
Hee Hee Hee Hee Hee!

Silly poo! Willy willy bum bum!
Willy willy BUM!
Hee Hee Hee Hee!

Big willy bum!
Heek Heek Hee Hee!! Hee!!

Hey! They're in our ROOM!
Willy willy!
Hee Hee!

GIDDOUT! Girls not allowed in!

You giddout! It's our room!
Ppllp!

Hee Hee Hee Hee!
Hee Hee Hee Hee

What is it?
Why you been laughing so much?
Hee Hee Hee Hee Hee!
Heek! Heek! Hee hee hee hee hee hee hee!

..HE..he just looked at my...hee hee...he just looked at my Willy!! Hee Hee Hee!
Hee hee hee!

Lessee! Go on...
Lessee

Hee Hee Hee Hee

mmp!

Hee Hee Hee! Hee Hee hee! hee hee! hee hee! hee!
Heek! Heek hee! Hee hee Hee hee!

Hee Hee Hee Ha ha ha heek heek hee! hee!
Hee Hee Hee Hee Hee Hee

s'not funny!

Alarms

Anything wrong, Belinda?
Nope... ..nuffing...

Nothing's the matter, Mum... Stop hassling me....

Bust-up with that louche, Saab-driving Alistair?.... Yes No
THE GUARD
Tax hopes

NOT Pregnant? Oh God!........ Yes No
Why did I do it?! Why!?

Herpes? .... Yes No

Other unmentionable Diseases?........ Yes No

Drink?... Yes No
Drugs?... Yes No
Debt?... Yes No

Trouble with the Police? Yes No
Oh, I've been so stupid!

Weltschmerz? ...... Yes No

Terminal Sulking? .... Yes No

Morning Mum!
!

TAMPAX

Pregnant? .... Yes No

Who worries about the Worriers?

Mm..you do look a bit rough, Wendy...

I'm FED UP! I'm exhausted!
I mean, it's TAKE, TAKE, TAKE...all the time!

I spend the whole time coping with THEIR problems!

...GEORGE, for instance....well, I KNOW it's worrying for him.....

..Now, listen, Wendy, will you...this is MY course the Assessor's damning.... He says "A ragbag of intellectual faddishness." ...PHILISTINE! Even my "La Pépinière de L'Apocalypse," gets it in the neck!.... He calls for a "caring system of structured modules".....
I give up!

...and then there's my mother...
...didn't EVEN put my buns on the stall!... ...I had to say to her, "That's the last time I'm supporting YOUR Bring & Buy!"......
...And now she...she cut me in Sainsbury's ...and she won't come and play Scrabble!
SNIFF
Oh dear!

...and Benji.......and Tamsin....
Bud I wanded you to buy me TRAINERS for school.. Bweurr..... NOT Gym shoes BOOPHOO

...And Mrs Taylor made me sit on the Trouble Seat all...
C.F.

....and Sophie.....
Course he'll ring you, Sophie... I'm sure he will...
HE WON'T!
SOB
...and why won't you led me have my ears pierced?

..and our babysitter:
Course he'll ring you, Trina...I'm sure he will...
He won't

...and the car...
Oh God, not more warning lights on all the time!
You've only just been serviced!

...and the cat....
PUSSY

There's a limit! I can't take any more!
I mean... NO ONE EVER says "Are you all right, Mum?"

...They NEVER ask!..... No one ever worries about ME! Never imagine that I might have my OWN worries...oh no!......

Have you got worries, Wendy?
Have I got worries!?

I'm worried about George... I'm worried about my mother... ..and Tamsin...and Sophie.... and the cat..and Trina...and...

To a TREE...

In a certain street, residents are on the *qui vive*.....
Excuse ME!
Oh GAWD, not another!

Look...about this TREE.....

Listen, lady, ORLRIGHT...Don't say another word, ORLRIGHT?.... WE ARE NOT CUTTING IT DOWN! ...ORLRIGHT?
...nor no other tree in this street ...ORLRIGHT?

We KNOW this is a CONSERVATION area, ORLRIGHT?...REPEAT: We are not cutting it down...We are LOPPING...ORLRIGHT?
LOPPING?!

Now LOOK! Look up there! That's an 'Ealth 'Azard, that is!
You want DODGY branches falling on your Volvo? Eh?

We're only doin' our job, ..ORLRIGHT? We're only lopping it a little bit...
Why only a little?

Why can't you cut the whole thing down?!
WOT?!

I MEAN CUT IT DOWN! THIS WHOLE, BLOODY TREE! I've had it up to HERE!! CUT it DOWN! DOWN!

I mean, have YOU LOOKED what's round this tree? Have YOU? HAVE YOU? What's THIS!?
Wull...lot of DOGS' WOSSNAME....
Poo Poo

YES! DOGS' MESS!!! That's what I put up with DAY IN...DAY OUT! Outside my kitchen window!! All over the KIDS' shoes... ...push chair wheels!!

Why ME? Why THIS tree? The dogs DO it...but it's the OWNERS' fault...
I've done EVERYTHING! ..cleaned up with ammonia... ..remonstrated...SHOUTED!

...I've taken polaroids of the dogs and their owners and stuck them in the window as a GALLERY of SHAME!

...I draw chalk circles round the messes and date them...

...I've sprayed them with GOLD paint to make them look prettier...!

But it's THIS TREE!! It's a MAGNET! I'm asking you...CUT it down! HACK it DOWN!
Diabolical Woman!

I think I shall never see A poem lovely as a tree... Poems are made by fools like me....
But DOGS can make a lavatr'ee...
GROAN

?
At the Poly, there is a rumour going round the staff canteen........

LEAVING us, George?
"Fresh fields and pastures new..?"
WOODS!
Woods?
It's fresh WOODS...not FIELDS...

Anyway, this is strictly entre-nous.....O.K?
See, I think it's a..a great opportunity for me.....
Oooh, GEORGE! Moving out into the sunrise industries, are we!?
Oooh!
HmM.

Cor... Well, well.... we'll be sorry to lose you.....
No No No! Don't get me wrong!

I haven't decided yet..whether to...

Haven't decided YET!? Och, Good God, man! Hardly a difficult decision!

I mean, ye've been teaching here quite a wee while, noo...
17 years...

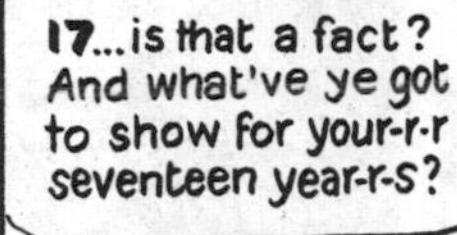
17...is that a fact? And what've ye got to show for your-r-r seventeen year-r-s?

Ye've got a wee space in the car park...

Ye're allowed free use of the Xer-rox....

Ye can make ootside calls BEFORE 1·00p.m...

You can claim your cassette tapes for dictating on EXPENSES
Ye've got a wee armchair in your office...
...and carpet tiles...

You can bring in a fan heater during cold weather...
You're allowed TICK here, in the canteen...and your own little MUG...
That's what you've got in 17 YEARS.
Yeah...I know...
GEORGE

So HOW can you THINK of giving all that up!!?
Don't do it, man!

The Absent minded Professor
FILM SOC
TONITE
KNIFE IN WATER

Afternoon..afternoon
Settle down, now everybody..... ...thank you...

Thank you, Martin... for the eleventh thousandth time, this is where I sit.... Remove the cans & chip papers, will you ...and if you're thinking of carrying on eating & drinking as usual, you can remove yourself from the room, thank you...and take THAT newspaper with you....

Sorry, George? Did you say something? I was reading....

!
Right, now...this afternoon, I want to discuss the Retreat from Social Reality...

Now, you remember our key dates...? ...1848..1870...
Hey!
Wot you do that for!?
Barbey d'Aur
Courbet
Do be quiet, Martin!

Look, you kicked me in the arse!
What!
You must be a mind reader!
Henri Mürger
EDMOND et Ju
de GONCO
Académie
How d'you know I'd think of doing a thing like that?

God! What more evidence do I need!!? You just...

You've never noticed before...
You've never done it before!
Oh, you'd be surprised... I do it constantly...whenever I see you...
?

I just don't know what you're doing at this Polytechnic, Martin... you never do any work...you just disrupt lectures...you're a distracting influence......

...No wonder I think of giving you a kick in the pants.... ...almost daily...
And today you DID!

What!?
You kicked me in the bum! You assaulted me!
GOD! I didn't!?
Did I?
Oh No!
In front of 24 witnesses

O God, Martin! I didn't mean to! Really!...It's unforgivable! I mean, I..I..
The PAPERS love this kind of...
Oh, you..you wouldn't... would you?!
...and of course the Union
Oh God!
What is it, George?
That BOY!
He's a NIGHTMARE!

Union Jakes

In the Brass Monk, the Webers are discussing Britain's decline with some Americans:
No, that's wrong!

. . . I mean, you're right, CLASS DISTINCTIONS here are still more than vestigial. . . . but they simply aren't as rigid as you've been implying. . . .

Hey, but you still haven't explained why you're so infantile.. I mean, your dirdy yumor... WHY are the Briddish so obsessed with that kinda anal stuff?
I mean... you're REtards!

Don't think we're MORE obsessed than anyone else... ...in Europe ...I mean, there's a long tradition of... of robust humour... Chaucer... Rabelais... . . . . but I wouldn't call us OBSESSED
Evening. Cod's eyes!

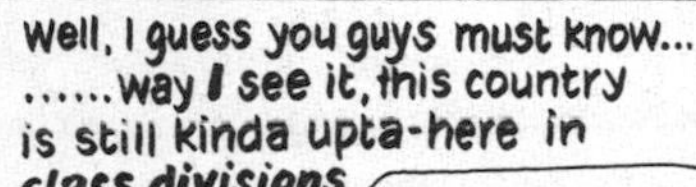

Well, I guess you guys must know... ......way I see it, this country is still kinda upta-here in class divisions

...like I said before, it's your main preoccupation...
...THAT...and toilet yumor

Class and what?
Toilet yumor ...you guys find toilets funny

Toilets?!

I don't talk about class... or toilets... . . . much . . .
Do you, Wendy?

I NEVER talk about toilets! HORRIBLE word!
Oh really Wendy!
IS it?

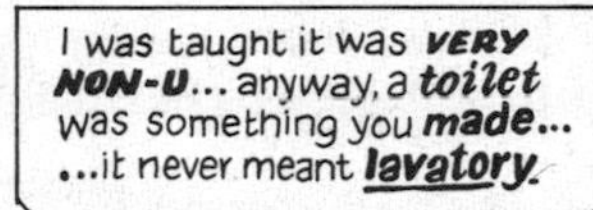

I was taught it was VERY NON-U... anyway, a toilet was something you made... ...it never meant lavatory.

Ooh, you say LAVATORY, do you?
...There's POSH!

Well, I say LOO sometimes.....

Oh, I hate LOO!
Yuppies say LOO...

...you see loo's more a middle class euphemism... and lavatory's more upper-class.. ..and toilet's...

At my prep school we used to call it the REARS

Rears, eh?
We called it the BOG....
We called it the AUNT

..Or the Slasher... ...or the JAKES..
I don't call it anything... I just go off to shake a tail feather ...or to pop a cork!
Her Her Her Heh Hehh

...or to go and change the barrel!
Her Her Haaa!

..pump the bilges...go and kill a hedge!
HAAAA! AHAHA HAHAA! HAAAA HAAA!

Omigard!
Retards!
Go where the big knobs hang out!
HAAAAA HAAHAA!

Giving Up

Edmund Heep is propping up the bar of the Castle & Ball...
That's another 2 pints of 3 star, please, Joy..

Like your sixth pint in a glass, Maurice?
Or d'you want it as an intravenous drip —and cut out the middleman!!?
AHAR HARHA! Har Har!!
Her her her!

Here, Edmund..... got a FAG on you? I'm gasping...

Gasping, are you? Oh dear!
Hey! You HAVEN'T given it up, have you?

No..but I've got the old faggeroons well under control!
What! YOU?!
Yes! I tell you! It's called self discipline!

It's a HABIT, smoking, isn't it? How many d'you smoke without thinking?
..Dunno
Well, there you are!

I, ...I have so disciplined myself......
..that, now, I NEVER smoke mindlessly.... but always for a reason...
I count every fag & make every fag count!
Result is... DRAMATIC reduction!!

What you do is, wrap the pack up, like this, in paper and rubber bands... so it's hard to get at.....

What's the pencil 'n' paper for?
..to LOG the time of the cigarette... and to answer the question you must always ask yourself: "Why do I want this fag? Why do I smoke?"

What, so you write: "because I feel TENSE"... or "made a right Horlicks of the sales returns"..... or...
You got it!

Let's have a look then...

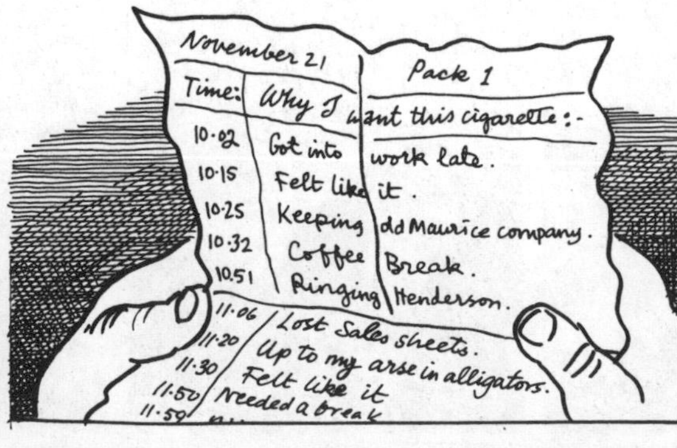
November 21
Pack 1
Time: Why I want this cigarette:-
10·02 Got into work late.
10·15 Felt like it.
10·25 Keeping old Maurice company.
10·32 Coffee Break.
10.51 Ringing Henderson.
11·06 Lost Sales sheets.
11·20 Up to my arse in alligators.
11·30 Felt like it
11·50 Needed a break

God! Two packs! And 19 just between tea-time and ... Now!
Not bad going, eh?
Have one on me.. I'm just off to shake a tail feather

New Minorities
Jelly Belli's

Oh brilliant! Rum'n'onion flavour!
Dad!
Let's see... what else...

...TV Din-Dins...
...Jelli-Foams....
...Porkalaties...
...Prawn Crakkles
...Bar-B-Q Insta Chips..

Ooh! Puffa-Cheez!
Brilliant shop, this
Caniver lolly, Dad?

And a lolly for the little lad...
That it, chasps?
Can I have a Drollie-Bun?

£17·60 for this lot! Stone me!
Still, one mustn't grumble when it's the REAL McCOY!!

...And, might I say, you're a real little oasis in the wilderness... proper treasure trove!
Oh well..we do aim to please our customers!

UNNATURAL FOODZ
C'mon Dad!
Abyssinia!

Tsk!
CRANKS!
SLUP!
SCRUNCH!
SSPWYLCH!

Croissant Neuf
VEGETARIAN CROISSANTS
The Natural Food Store
Health Foods
FREE RANGE EGGS
ORGANIC VEG
SESAME MILK
LEGUMES
PULSES
KRUSKA
RICES
KEFIR
NUTS
THE GRAINERY
73
WHOLE GRAIN BREAD
UNNATURAL FOODZ
77 Herbalis
Called me a CRANK, did you?
Steady on, Jules
That geezer's asking for a good breavin' on...
Go on, Jules
adidas
hHAAAAA
Thickener E410
Colors E102 E110 E122
Acidity Regulator
E331
E471

SENSES & Sensibilities
Fizzz
150
SPEEDBURGER
HamBurgers
156 Blast Records
Blast Records
1. Sight
Oh, look! That's nice!
Ooh Look! Lovely Pink!
Ooh Look
Oh Look! Matching Skirts!
Look
2. Smell
Ooh! Smell! Onions! Mmm....
LEWIS'
3. Taste
SPEEDBURGER
Burgers
Munch Munch
Munch Munch
Slurp Slurp
BLAST! RECORDS
4. Hearing
Oh, Listen! Barry Manilow!
Oh YES! LISTEN!
5. Touch
Oh, FEEL!
Oh, just FEEL it!
Oh, it feels GORGEOUS!
1. Unsightly
2. Smelly
OSBORNES
3. Distasteful
Osborne's
4. Unheard
Excuse me...
5. Untouchable
Fizzz

Posy Simmonds 1984

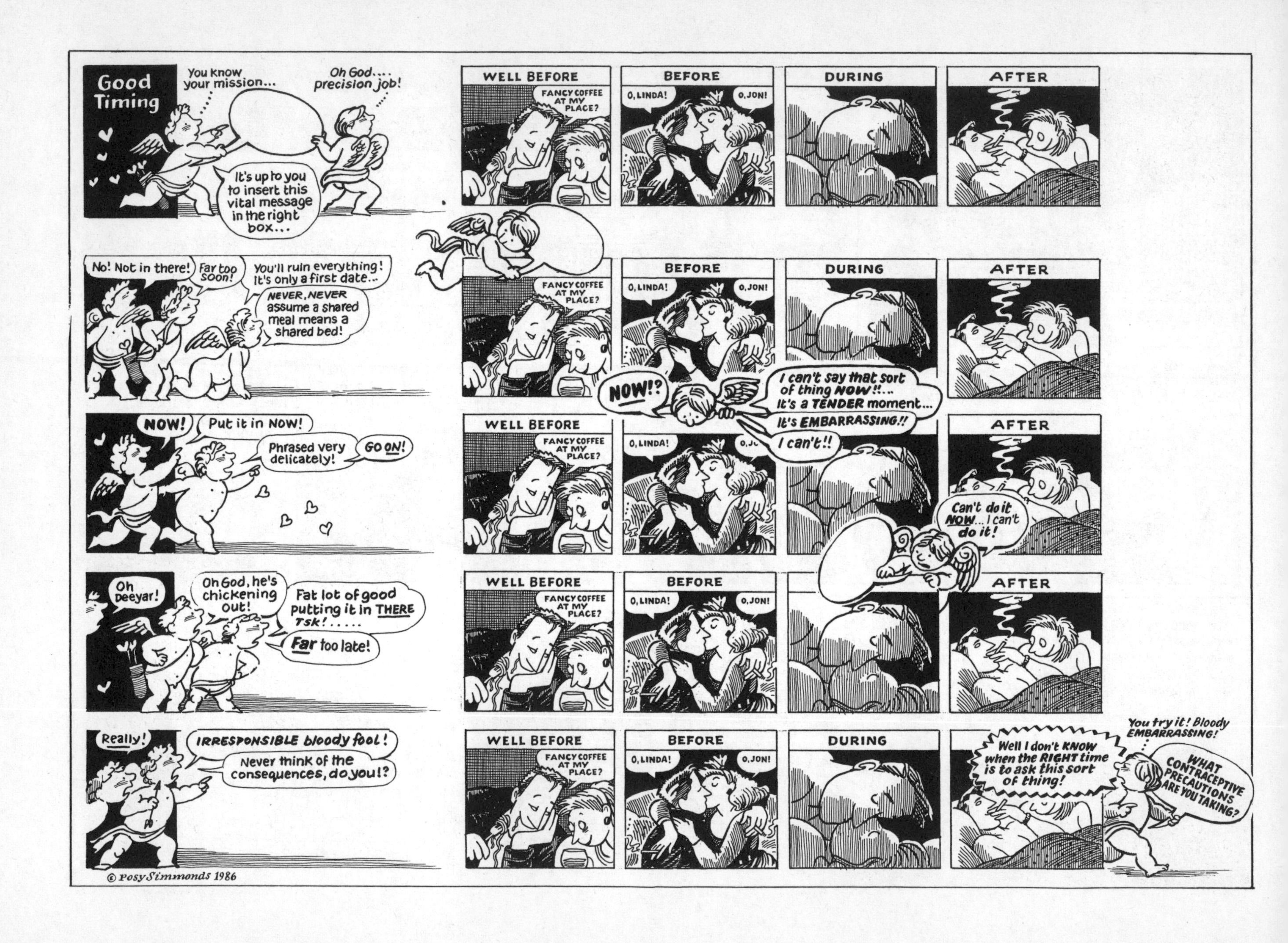
Good Timing
You know your mission...
Oh God.... precision job!
It's up to you to insert this vital message in the right box...
WELL BEFORE
FANCY COFFEE AT MY PLACE?
BEFORE
O, LINDA!
O, JON!
DURING
AFTER
No! Not in there!
Far too soon!
You'll ruin everything! It's only a first date...
NEVER, NEVER assume a shared meal means a shared bed!
FANCY COFFEE AT MY PLACE?
BEFORE
O, LINDA!
O, JON!
DURING
AFTER
NOW!
Put it in NOW!
Phrased very delicately!
GO ON!
WELL BEFORE
FANCY COFFEE AT MY PLACE?
O, LINDA!
NOW!?
I can't say that sort of thing NOW!!... It's a TENDER moment...
It's EMBARRASSING!!
I can't!!
AFTER
Can't do it NOW... I can't do it!
Oh Deeyar!
Oh God, he's chickening out!
Fat lot of good putting it in THERE tsk!.....
Far too late!
WELL BEFORE
FANCY COFFEE AT MY PLACE?
BEFORE
O, LINDA!
O, JON!
AFTER
Really!
IRRESPONSIBLE bloody fool!
Never think of the consequences, do you!?
WELL BEFORE
FANCY COFFEE AT MY PLACE?
BEFORE
O, LINDA!
O, JON!
DURING
Well I don't KNOW when the RIGHT time is to ask this sort of thing!
You try it! Bloody EMBARRASSING!
WHAT CONTRACEPTIVE PRECAUTIONS ARE YOU TAKING?

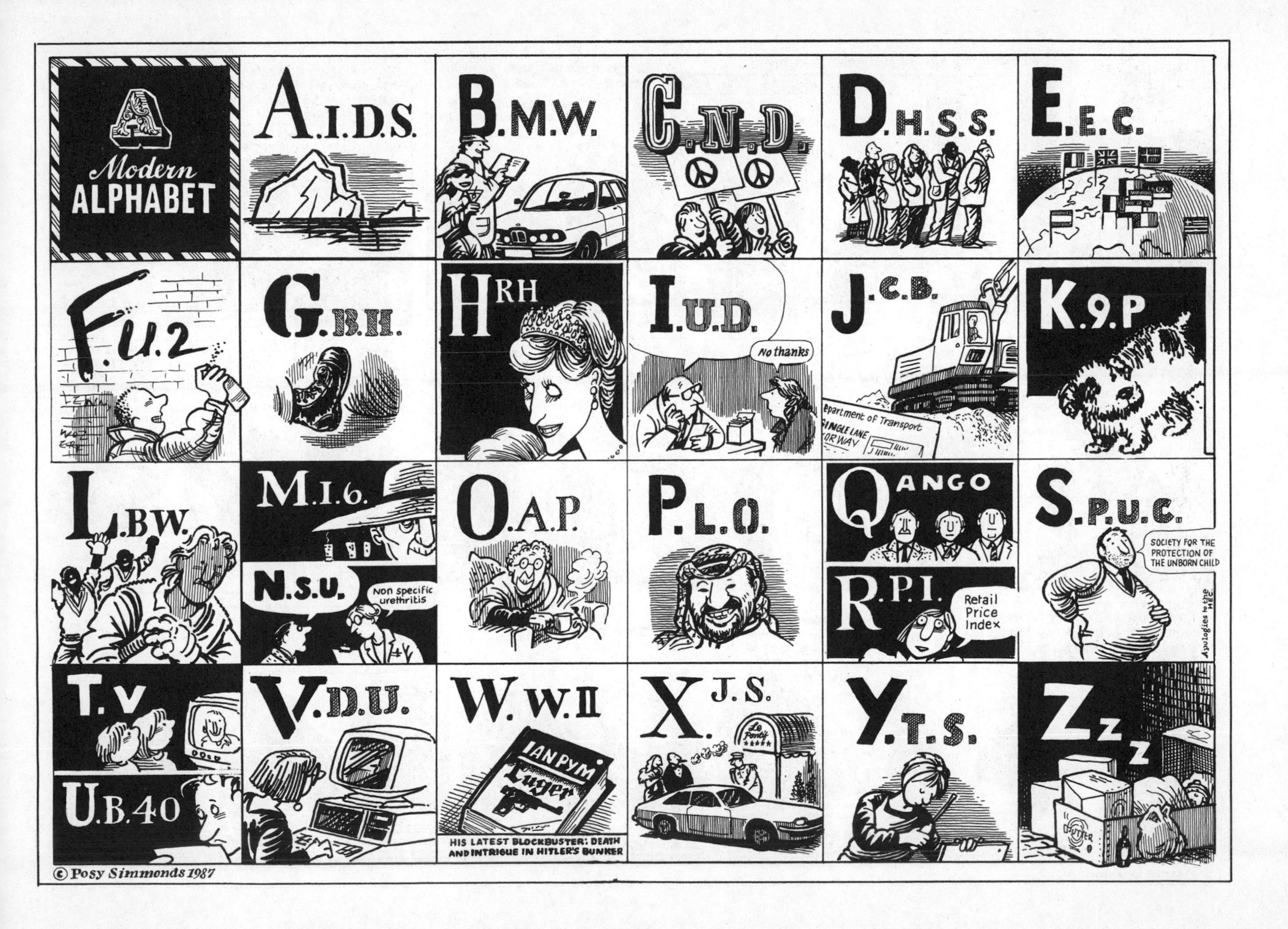

Modern ALPHABET
A.I.D.S.
B.M.W.
C.N.D.
D.H.S.S.
E.E.C.
F.U.2
G.B.H.
HRH
I.U.D.
No thanks
J.C.B.
K.9.P
L.B.W.
M.I.6.
N.S.U.
Non specific urethritis
O.A.P.
P.L.O.
QANGO
R.P.I.
Retail Price Index
S.P.U.C.
SOCIETY FOR THE PROTECTION OF THE UNBORN CHILD
T.V
U.B.40
V.D.U.
W.W.II
IAN PYM
Luger
HIS LATEST BLOCKBUSTER: DEATH AND INTRIGUE IN HITLER'S BUNKER
X.J.S.
Y.T.S.
Zzz

School Steps

What Money can buy

No, Bev! Really?
a cellular phone
£1000!

What's this, Wendy!? Bev tells me she's being PRIVATELY educated!
Really?

She certainly isn't!...Well,... not....
I AM Mum!
Oh, Wendy, Wendy!
Come on!

It's ALL RIGHT, Wendy....... now, now!

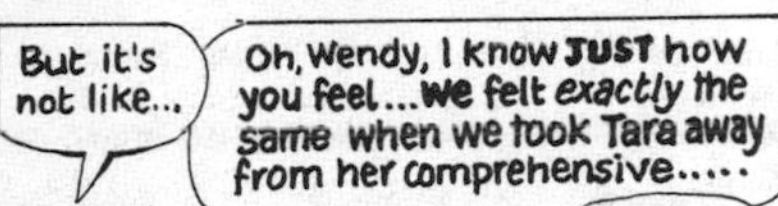
But it's not like...
Oh, Wendy, I know JUST how you feel...we felt exactly the same when we took Tara away from her comprehensive.....

It was absolute AGGERS!

Don't feel BAD, ..honestly...
It's not HERESY any more... We've ALL done it...
EVERYONE round here's.....

I mean...you HAVE to think of the children.... Why should we make them suffer for our principles?

It's not fair....Tara HATED Fletcher Montacute...absolutely LOST in those huge classes!
And those boys! She never learnt ANY Maths at all...the girls could never get NEAR the computer terminals.....

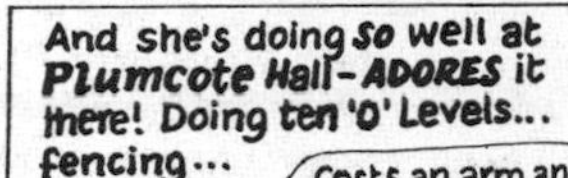
And she's doing so well at Plumcote Hall - ADORES it there! Doing ten 'O' Levels... fencing...

Costs an arm and a leg each term, but...well...
I mean, I know, au fond, it's wrong...but...
It is wrong!

It's GOT to be wrong to BUY privilege!
How ARE the state schools going to get any better, if the middle classes have no interest in putting pressure on the system?
We all ought to contribute to the social mix...

For all its faults, Bev's staying put at Thomas Crawley...I feel very strongly about it.
Oh, but I THOUGHT Bev said she was...

Oh, THAT?
Well, yes, she was er...falling behind a bit...and...yes... she does have a bit of help at home...
Aha! Little PRIVATE COACHING, eh?

Not like that at all!... ...it's just, well... Crispin Naylor pops in and..er... helps her with her Maths and Science in the evenings....that's all...
For M·O·N·E·Y?

Well, yes... we DO pay him.... I mean, I feel sorry for these graduates...he hasn't found a proper job yet...
I see-ee

Told you I had a PRIVATE TUTOR!

Hmm...
All you need is Love??

Q: What is W.O.T.?

Here is a typical W.O.T. case:

Once addicted, recovery is often unpleasant, involving severe withdrawal symptoms. This man had a 92 hour-a-week work habit.....

Do you plead pressure of work to avoid irksome situations?

Do you bore others with your preoccupation with work?

Do you cause unecessary stress to the unwaged?

Housework isn't REAL work. Do you agree?

Do you think about work in bed?

Rough Winds do blow....

The Webers have taken advantage of the Bank Holiday to make an excursion into the countryside, with family and friends......
Motorway

Having reviewed the Spring.....
How much further?
It's raining again!

...they repair to a hostelry....
I'll just give these to George
OK, Tom

Yes, wasn't that lovely..seeing the buds...
..I mean, in town, the kids're completely CUT OFF.. I mean, they just can't sort of get to experience...the THRILL of each season, can they?

..and it's so good for them to see a bit of.. folklore.... ..tradition....
God...I'm worried about George...
Oh Yes!

..well, bought him a pie and a pint... ..& merely remarked "This is the life!" ...and he BIT my HEAD off!
?
!

Yes! He went on & on!

What's so bloody wonderful about it?
...Just another day WASTED!
Bloody HOLIDAYS!
I've got to behave as though I'm RELAXED.. & I can't relax, 'cause I'm too busy thinking it's MONDAY... Just makes a great DENT in my lecture programme... I'll more or less have to give the last one AGAIN, so the students can pick up the thread... Tsk! ...Oh God!

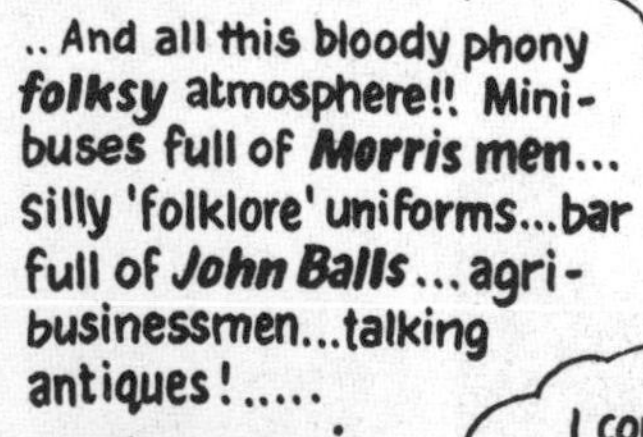

.. And all this bloody phony folksy atmosphere!! Mini-buses full of Morris men... silly 'folklore' uniforms...bar full of John Balls... agri-businessmen...talking antiques!.....

I could be wading through that pile of theses assessments
You go off, Tom... don't mind me... You go and enjoy yourself...

Oh don't take any notice...

...he always behaves like that, when it's his turn to sit with the kids.....
BAR

The House-Keeping

You know Bryony was on time this morning! ... taken the kids to the park already!
uh

Oh God! NOT AGAIN! No muesli!
What did you say?
I said: Bryony was on time today...... First time for ages I won't be late for work....

Tsk! Look, it's all gone...think you could get some today?
Just as easy for you to get it...

Never anything to EAT in this bloody house!

Patrick...?
What?
...I've been thinking.... What if we did without Bryony looking after the kids? ....

EH?

What if I gave up my job...and stayed at home full time?
Don't be daft!
What about your career?

Some career! Dogsbody in an art gallery!
But it's IMPORTANT to you! Gets you out of the house....
Gives you financial independence
Anyway...we need the money...
But most of what I earn, goes on paying Bryony!

You think of it, Patrick....... I could be here...running the house properly...we wouldn't run out of muesli....
SNIFF SNIFF

...I'd be able to shop properly.....
...have proper meals ready...
...No more dashing out to the take-away!

I'd be here ALL the time..... No more dashing back from work so Bryony can go...
No more hassles on her day off.....

No more of her ponky cigarettes...

No more weekends doing housework.... ...wouldn't have to cook!

...my shirts ironed...buttons put on...clothes taken to the cleaners...no more mountains of filthy socks...the BOG cleaned.....

You quite like the idea, don't you?
M..... mm...

April Foo-ool!

Pilgrimage: Whan that Aprille with his shoures sote, The droght of March hath perced to the rote, Than longen folk to goon on Diets, at places of Purgation:

Many are they who embark, who have sat by flesh pots & eaten bread and have waxed fat....

And others, stiff-necked people, full of affliction, & those that are vain, yet full of care....

Each shall put on loose raiment...

...and go before those in judgement over them. For their sins are numbered,

....and many and various are the ways of chastisement.

And thenceforward, five nights & days shall they repent, eschewing all meat and wine,

...mortifying the flesh and meditating on the folly of their ways.

And some do undergo a fiery torment.....

...and do cast out devils...

...and others do force their joints to go off like pistols and their hamstrings to cry out...

And others do confess diverse heresies and are shriven.

Posy Simmonds ©

And when the days of their tribulation are accomplished, they are absolved.

10 stone 2! Jolly good!

Most have endured great losses. But some are still like great Bulls of Bashan; And some have masticated secretly, and are found out.

And then all do depart, & break their fast, and go on their way rejoicing.....

OLD ARCADIA
Lud! How Picturesque!
What jocund rusticity!
GLEANER'S COTTAGE with children playing
D'you Peasants mind just sodding off DOWN WIND a bit!?
Poo!
But oi live here!
New Arcadia
Ooh Look!
Aaah!
Isn't that QUAINT!
Gorgeous old world scene!
So peaceful!
Aaah!
Isn't that a PICTURE!
Rustic Heritage Tours
WEEKENDER'S COTTAGE with children playing
Oi were born there!
Aye...Nice picture if you can afford it...
Huh!
But you've got council houses...
Why don't you just homeward plod-off!
© Posy Simmonds 1986

Different Species

What fun it is discovering the countryside near one's second home....
Oh look, darling! What's this one?

...Erm...this is it...Vernal Squill...
...pale blue, with bracts...grassy cliff slopes....and it flowers...
...April-May...
No! Don't PICK them, Toby!
Wild Flowers

..that is...Valerian...leaves ovate....
...walls, rocks, banks...Flowers: June-Aug
Don't PICK it, Rachel!
Really! How many times!

It's Common Scurvy Grass....
...long stalked...cliffs and shores...Flowers: May-Aug.....

Rachel! For the last time! If you pick things, there won't BE any next year!
Wild Flowers

Yes..that's Ransom's Wood Garlic...
...common in damp woods....
Flowers: April-June....
Now, don't pick ANYthing else!

Deadly Nightshade! Of course!
...common woods...etc..etc...
berries VERY poisonous!

Fancy a jar over there?...we haven't tried that one yet, have we?
O, let's!

THAT'S easy...that's Bindweed...

Dry white wine, please darling...
You wait out there, Toby
Ooh!
It's Creeping Village Blight..
Common in rural areas
Puts local house prices up
Guilty, viscid manner...
Children can be poisonous
Earns £35,000 a year
Flowers only occasionally, mainly week-ends, Bank and school holidays...
...and sometimes at Midnight Mass, Dec 24, & Easter Day....
Needs babysitters (£2·00 an hour)
Needs grass mown (£5·00 an hour...)
Needs mail forwarding, meters read, an eye kept on the place...£20 p.w....
Burst pipes dealt with...£10 an hour.
Pick 'em for all they're worth!

As I awoke this morning....
...I heard a funny thing.....

Pigeons rutting on my sill,
.... I thought:

A sunbeam burst upon my floor,
And gilded every crumb.....
And old clipped nails & dead skin scales
Lay glinting in the sun.....

The sun is up, the World is young,
The blowfly's on the wing......

The dust is gambolling in the glare...

O, sap must rise....
And Spring must come...

And breathe regeneration...
But, woe is me!....I've work undone:

Three idle years of student bliss
Have nearly passed away...

And I must hand this b*gg*r in
A fortnight from today.....

When, round about this time of year,
One hears a student sing.........

Family Planning
Trish Wright & her step daughter, Jocasta, pore over a distant relative's wedding photographs:
But who are all these people?
That's not Jon's parents, surely?
Ooh look... they've sent wedding cake... & a plan of their Dream House!
Who the HELL are they, Jocasta?
Who's THIS?
Look: that's Jon's REAL mum... that's his stepfather..... ...THAT's his REAL father.. that's his stepmother... that's Sara's REAL mother, Aunt Bunny.... and that's Aunt Bunny's new bloke... THAT's Uncle Simon, Sara's real father... that's his new wife... that's the Dream House... that's the Utility Room... that's...
OK! OK!
Our New House!
UTILITY ROOM
KITCHEN
HALL
All those step-parents! Look at 'em! All being super-matey together!
God, how grisly!
Why!?
What's grisly, Trish? It's The Family.... Family Life... it's a very precious institution....
... It's the only thing we've got ...our only buttress against Life's slings and arrows...
Our New House!
Kitchen
Lounge
Bed
.. And it's been under attack from the Welfare State for far too long! But, thank God that's over... The Family's triumphed! From now on, we can nurture and succour our own....
Tsk!
But Trish.. the New Family has arrived! Here it is in embryo, in this photo!
.. And it's a wonderful thing this family of the Future! ...founded on THRIFT.... HARD WORK... SELF-RELIANCE..... and NO SOCIAL SERVICES!
Does my heart good to think of Jon & Sara in a few years' time... Jon, the HEAD and Sara, the HEART of their family of eight... forced to care for Aunt Bunny...& Aunt Bunny's bloke..& Uncle Simon...& Uncle Simon's wife...& Jon's REAL mother ...and...
Granny Annexe
Kitchen
Bath
Hall
Lounge
Bedroom
Bed
Bed
Granny Annexe 2
STEP-PARENT PORTAKABIN
STEP-PARENT PORTAKABIN 2
Bed room
Bed room
Bed room

The Game of Happy Families

Please...is Mrs Gleam, the Government's Dream, at home?
Yes! Mrs Gleam is at home!

Mrs Gleam, the Government's Dream is always at HOME... ...where a mother belongs!
Bless her!
Thank you...Oh, isn't she charming!

:SIGH: If only ALL mothers were like her, Society's ills would disappear in a twinkling!

..Now, please: would little Miss Gleam be at home?
Yes! She's at home!
...Here she is, cuddling her panda....

Thanks awfully!...Roy, P.L.E.A.S.E, by any chance, are the two Master Gleams about the house?
Indeed they ARE! ...romping in the rumpus room!
Ooh! The naughty pixies!

"TIBBLES" GLEAM
MASTERS B&G GLEAM
MRS GLEAM
MISS GLEAM
Oh, what a super family! What a gorgeous little home!

...And, FINALLY, please, Denzil, dear...
...is Mr Gleam, the Government's Dream, at home?

Er...Mr Gleam, the £25,000 a year pater familias?
Er...he's NOT at home...he's gone off with his P.A., Miss Toser....

What!?

He's getting a divorce and going abroad...and he's planning to be a naughty fellow about paying maintenance...
Right... now it's my turn...

Just a minute!
It's not FAIR!
Look here!
Look at my hand! Mr Gleam's ruined it!
Surely you've got another breadwinner!

Sorry...I mean there's young Mr Bang, the Broker...and Mr Divorce, father of three...
...but they're both looking for younger women....

SOTTO VOCE
Mrs Gleam'll just have to get a job, that's all...
Er..yes..although her marvellous mothering talents, perhaps, won't be the greatest draw in the market place

And WHO'll look after the children!!?
Oh, deary me!..oh you're right...Mrs Gleam should stay at home...um...
...on..um.. supplementary benefit...
Yes

...A single-parent family! ....social nightmare!
It's the luck of the game, Margaret!

Dear Agony Aunt.... I am the mother of three small children... I look quite young, but feel a hundred.....

I live high above the city. The place is cold, filthy and verminous and the air polluted. I fear for my children's health.

I was led to believe that the rôle of **Mother** was **sacred** and **hallowed**, that its duties were of the most **vital importance** to Society.... and that people would look up to me in reverence...

But they do not. Beneath me the World goes about its **real** concerns, as if I do not exist....

I spend my long domestic days in isolation.... mute, passive, without identity.....

People only take notice of me when I become **unstable**.... it's not my fault – the traffic shakes my foundations.....

Then, **the Authorities** call me a **Danger to Society**... and rail against mothers as the source of every social evil...

They are threatening to take away my Child Benefit and replace it with a means-tested credit.... I feel I'm **cracking up** completely....... Please help.... **Mother of Three**.

We were talking in the pink and gold, second floor drawing room of her London home...a lovely, lived-in room, full of the Art Deco bric-a-brac which she & her company director husband, Ron Grossman, have collected on their many trips abroad. Besides the London home, there is an 18th century, Wiltshire mansion and a luxuriously converted barge, moored at Bray-on-Thames.

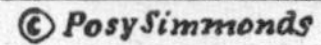

FORTRESS BRITONS

These other Edens, these demi-paradises...these Fortresses, armed by Britons for themselves, against intrusion and the hand of war......

....This happy breed of men..... ...these little worlds....these precious homes, set in a greenish belt which serves them in the office of a wall......

Or as a moat, defensive to a house...against the envy of less happier folk...These blessed plots! These earths, this England!

DRIED-ON DIRT:

YELLOW WAXY BUILD-UP:

CRUSTED CORNERS:

HEAVY SOILING

TELL-TALE TOILET TIDE-MARK:

RADIOACTIVE DUST:

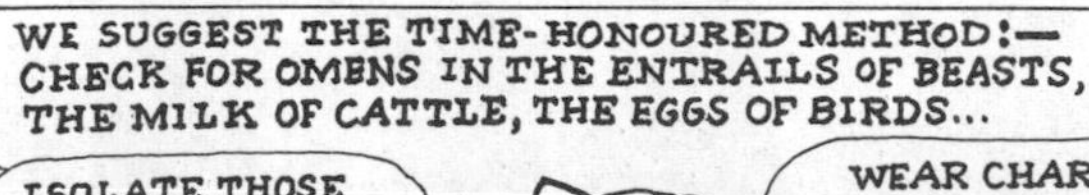

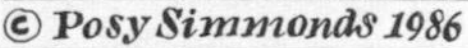

1. Heresies and Blasphemies:

2. Supplication:

3. Heavenly Intervention:

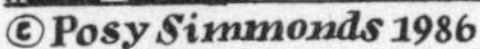

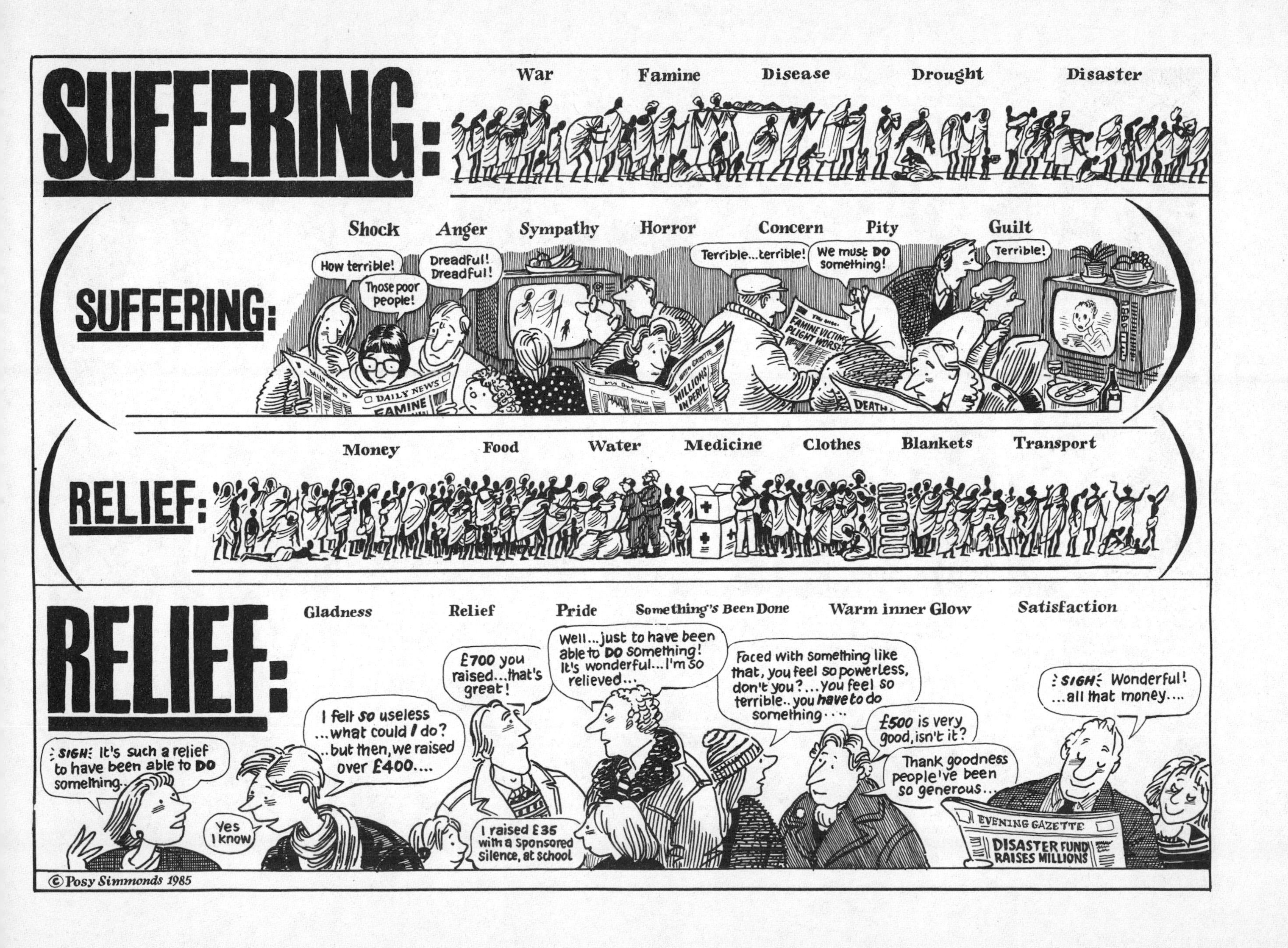
SUFFERING:
War
Famine
Disease
Drought
Disaster
SUFFERING:
Shock
Anger
Sympathy
Horror
Concern
Pity
Guilt
How terrible!
Those poor people!
Dreadful! Dreadful!
Terrible...terrible!
We must DO something!
Terrible!
DAILY NEWS
FAMINE
FAMINE VICTIMS PLIGHT WORSE
MILLIONS IN PERIL
DEATH
RELIEF:
Money
Food
Water
Medicine
Clothes
Blankets
Transport
RELIEF:
Gladness
Relief
Pride
Something's Been Done
Warm inner Glow
Satisfaction
SIGH: It's such a relief to have been able to DO something..
Yes I know
I felt so useless ...what could I do? ..but then, we raised over £400....
£700 you raised...that's great!
I raised £35 with a sponsored silence, at school
Well...just to have been able to DO something! It's wonderful...I'm so relieved...
Faced with something like that, you feel so powerless, don't you?...you feel so terrible.. you have to do something....
£500 is very good, isn't it?
Thank goodness people've been so generous...
SIGH: Wonderful! ...all that money....
EVENING GAZETTE
DISASTER FUND RAISES MILLIONS

...OVER sixty quid a head! Poor you, it makes you feel GUILTY, doesn't it, that a lot of people find it utterly OBSCENE your spending their equivalent of six months' dole money on a single meal.....

And I'm sure you also realise that a family of four could make two decent meals out of what you've all left on your plates and side dishes....

Don't feel GUILTY! I want you to know that it's NOT wrong to indulge yourself... to give pleasure to your friends... you WORK hard... you deserve it!

Restaurants like this are highly labour intensive... you're helping employ people... you're helping to maintain standards of cooking in Britain...

There have to be some people in our society to help maintain touchstones of EXCELLENCE... ...& that's what you do...

Weights and Measures
FAT PRIDE

Can't get over HOW much weight you've lost!
How've you done it?!
You're a little WRAITH!
Diet and exercise....

...and cutting out all that, you know, crap...about having heavy bones and a low metabolic rate.....

Quite frankly, I was FAT because I was a complete TOTAL PIG!...and I ate too much!

...and I mean, I WAS FAT!
O. you weren't!
Oh I WAS!....... FAT-FAT-FAT!

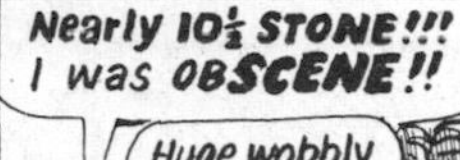
Nearly 10½ STONE!!! I was OBSCENE!!

Huge wobbly bum....

...great, white saddle bags of LARD here... Eeuch!
Yeah?
Puhh! Should see mine!

I mean! My THIGHS overlapped at the top!
Oh THAT! That's GROSS!
Euuu!

And all that flodge you get flopping over bra straps!
GROSS!
I had it! I had it! Euu!
And under-arm dingle-dangle!
Euu!

I was obscene...obscene! Well, I've still got to lose a bit here...see, I can still pinch an inch...look...

That's nothing!

God, Patrick! Better watch that! Don't want to end up a great, obscene...
PAT PAT!

Great, obscene what?

Oh er...
A...a great, obscene...scrawny, wizened-up DIET-BORE, you know, all calorie-consciousness-raising... ...rumbling tummy and veggie-breath and toast-rack ribs
all thin & weedy..

Yeah, all skin & bones . . .
You know, it's so neurotic this media-con about being THIN!
It's obscene!
....You know, people...especially women...should be whatever size they feel like!
And BIG people often have such lovely skins ...lovely creamy....
You know, Renoir...
That's not what you say behind my backside!

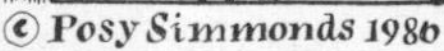

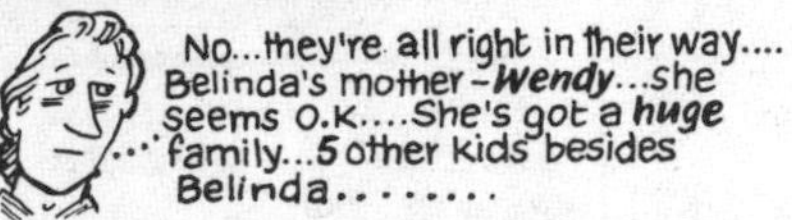

What's *he* like... ..Belinda's father?

Oh! COMPLETELY BATS!

..You know, *TOYS* in the attic....

JUST
past it

Well, I think the message is getting through.....
...one hears the most unlikely people talking about condoms now, doesn't one?

Yes, everywhere!
P'raps I'll try the goat cheese
Is it very goaty?

But they're still forecasting 200,000 infected with the virus by 1988, aren't they?
And that's tip of the iceberg... ...tip of the iceberg.....
...so I've read somewhere....

Poor young people... I feel so sorry for them... ...IMAGINE their sex lives......
Yep! Puts the kibosh on the old wild oats
Glad my salad days are long gone.....

NOT talking about wild oats...
..I'm saying..in future, even two unspotted virgins'll have the screens rushed round and a blood test or two zapped on them, before they hold hands...

Mm...imagine what their parties'll be like...PARANOIA!
No more smooching in corners....
Oh yes...kissing's in the doghouse, now, isn't it...
Is it?

Well, not sort of hello/goodbye kissing...that's O.K....
There is a theory that the AIDS virus has been around a lot longer than the last few years...or so I read somewhere.......
Ah
EH?!

Whaat?
How long?
Eh?
Well...there's a lot they don't know about lymph nodes & their pathology.... ...you know, the electron microscope hasn't been around for ever.....

But, AIDS...how long's that been around?
Before 1969, say..?
Well, could be....but they just don't KNOW.... ...I mean, it's only conjecture....
Oh God

Oh really, Belinda..... don't let's start being DEPRESSING!

Nature abhors a Vacuum

So...both your kids'll be at school ALL day in September?
Yes! Isn't it wonderful when they reach a civilised age?!
Can you bring the cakes, Wendy?

I mean, I know they're lovely when they're littler......

Orlando
Kate.
... but it's such hard work..... all those broken nights... NAPPIES...

...all those zoo-like smells..... sweaters covered in dribble....
Mm...these look good
Patisserie Svette

... and never having a minute alone... except if you lock yourself in the bog...

...and not being able to leave them with people ...and feeling guilty if you do...
Kate

And people treating you like a half-wit & being all condescending when you say you don't work OUTSIDE the home.....

...and, really, you just feel so flaked out the whole time...
LICK!

Ah...it's a real relief to have got them to this stage...really civilised ...I can't believe it...

..I shall have these long uninterrupted mornings... afternoons too...& I only have to do the school run one week a month..
So what will you do? Go back to teaching...do a PhD... do the hospital Mobile library?

..thing is... thought I'd have another baby...

Cheerful Thoughts

They **WHAT!?** ***Hit*** an old lady!!?
Yes! Two seven year olds...at the twins' school....

God! All this **VIOLENCE**! What a world to bring a child into!
Don't worry, Jane...I'm sure yours is going to be a model baby...
How can you be so sure?

Kids from nice homes are just as likely to turn out
EH?
NICE homes!? *Meaning* ***what***, *exactly?*

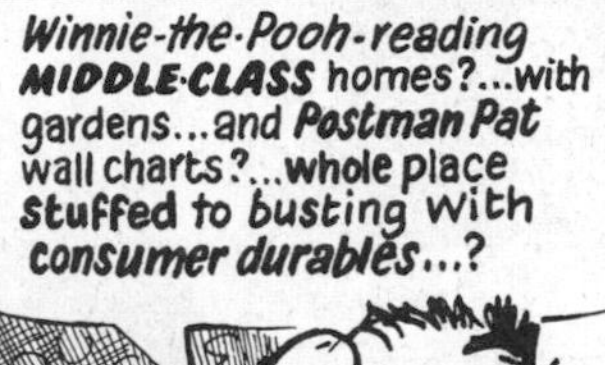
Winnie-the-Pooh-reading ***MIDDLE-CLASS*** homes?...with gardens...and ***Postman Pat*** wall charts?...whole place ***stuffed to busting*** with ***consumer durables***...?

That what you mean?

Oh ***shuddup***, George....I mean **ANY** sort of home where the ***parents CARE***... where the kids are taught to consider other people...where they learn ***certain values***...

Ah, yes..where they learn ***CERTAIN VALUES***.... which are then shot to smithereens, soon as they switch on **TV**..or step outside the *front* door!
Oh.. ***Cheerful!***
Fat chance **CERTAIN VALUES** have in our ***HORRIBLE, VIOLENT AGGRESSIVELY MATERIALISTIC*** *society!*

Well, *of course* **NURTURE** has a lot to do with how kids turn out......
...***and NATURE***...
...and ***CHANCE***....

But I'm sure a lot of ***NURTURE*** helps...you'll be ***terrific*** in that department....
See, ***thanks***..

Oh, **JANE**'s here! ***How nice! How ARE*** *you?*
Had a good snooze, Mummy?

You look ***blooming!***...
..and ***how's*** the **BUMP?**
Doesn't time fly!
Oh, he's fine!

Oh, it's a **HE**, is it?
Yes, they could tell from my amniocentesis test....
...He **KICKS** like anything!

Aaah! That's *lovely!* Good ***strong kicks!***.. P'raps he's going to be ***Nureyev!*** ..or a ***FOOTBALLER***...! ...or..or a little ***Football hooligan!!!***
HA HA! *Ah Dear!*

Oh..
Have I said something wrong?

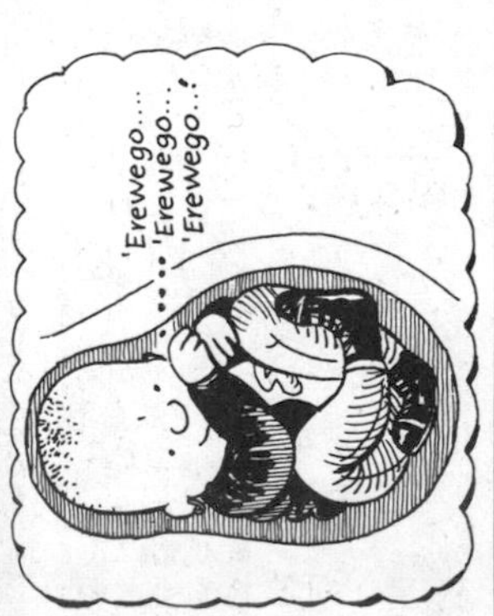
'Erewego...
...'Erewego...
'Erewego...!

babaware

babaware

70 - 80 cm

0 - 6 month

SOCKS

babaware

cash

Excuse me.... THIS... I'm not sure if he needs the 80 or the 90 centimetres...

For him, is it?..Your little grandson?
I BEG your pardon?

Not my grandson!! He's my SON!!
Oh sorry!
Really!
Didn't mean...

Well, I know it's second time round...um...my second wife.... but I'm not all THAT...um.... I mean, YES, I do have an older family...but I'm certainly not a grandfather....

No No, No!

um...well, I think you'll find the 80 cm is right for him...
Thank you

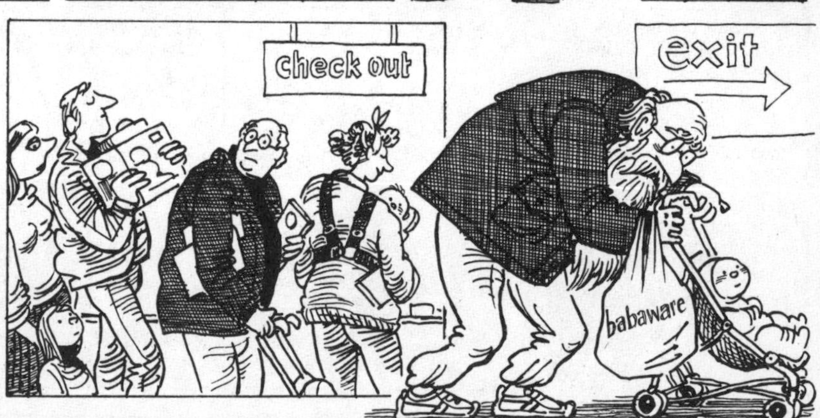
check out
exit
babaware

Always in the NEWS

...Police warned all women in the area to be especially on their guard...The man is described as being in his twenties, wearing a maroon anorak and fawn slacks...and driving a light blue, hatch-back car.......

....Two men, who robbed and attacked a pensioner in her home in Sefton Botbole, were each given seven year gaol sentences today, by a judge at the.....
Tsk!
SIGH

...A man is now helping police with their enquiries, after the discovery of a half-naked, woman's body was found on wasteland at King's
Tsk

...A gang of four men master-minded the hijacking of a five ton lorry in North London, and made off with £200,000 worth of electrical
NEW

oughton United fans went on the rampage after their team lost two-nil to
arrests
Tsk!

...Police are now considering fresh evidence in the hunt for the killer of six year old Gilli
NEW

body was found last July in
sexually assaulted
Tsk!
Tsk!
Tsk!
MEN!

Think I'll just go and give Benji his cough mixture....

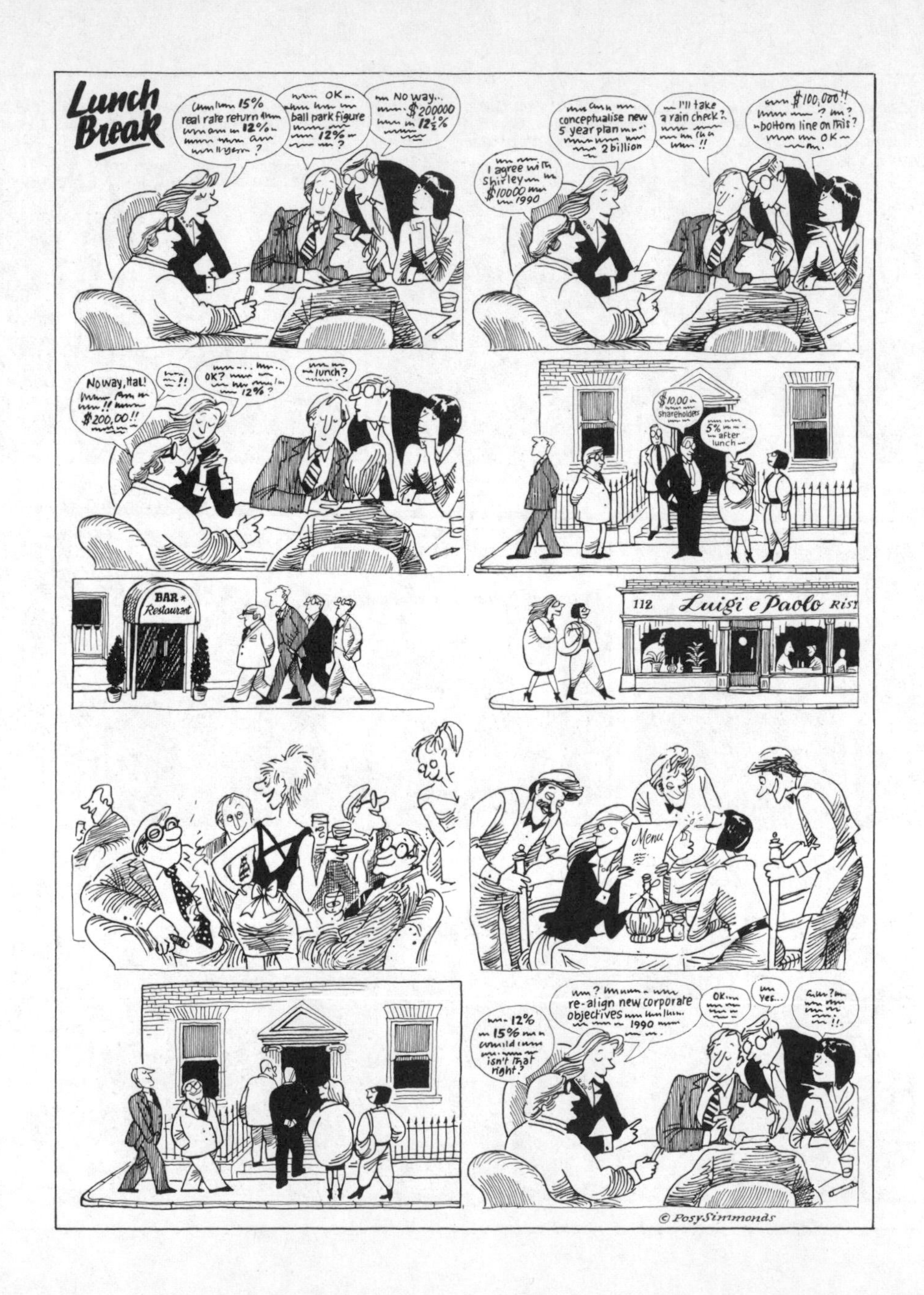
Lunch Break
15%
real rate return
12%
?
OK...
ball park figure
12%
?
No way...
$200000
12½%
I agree with
Shirley
$10000
1990
conceptualise new
5 year plan
2 billion
I'll take
a rain check?
!!
$100,000!!
? ?
bottom line on this?
OK
No way, Hal!
!!
$200,00!!
!!
OK?
12%?
lunch?
$10.00
shareholders
5%
after
lunch
BAR
Restaurant
112
Luigi e Paolo
RIST
Menu
12%
15%
isn't that
right?
?
re-align new corporate
objectives
1990
OK
Yes...
?
!!
© Posy Simmonds

God, I mean! What a WEEK!!! ...and 9 last night till 5 this morning!...I mean...they just don't understand what it's like!
Dunno how you stand it

Hair Today

6 CHAS. CUTLER
GENTS' HAIRDRESSER

That's it...right..magic... ...*student* are we?
Yeah

Nice ***Rockabilly*** you got here. if I might say so..
Keeping the length, are you?
Nuh..want it cut..something a bit STRAIGHT

Short back & sides?
Right?
Magic!
Nuh! Not *that* Straight!

Ooh, your wish my command, chief!

Anything you like from **A** to **Z**...
Affro... **B**eatle... **C**ollege Boy **D**uck's arse **E**lvis...
Gor, no... Not a D.A!

..or **F**lat top...**G**uardsman ...**H**ippy...**I**vy League...
Tsk! No..

...er... **K**ojak...er...**M**od.... **M**ohican..**N**ew Wedge
Fancy a *New Wedge*?

..or, there's **O.O.T**...**P**sychobilly...**Q**uiff... **R**ude Boy...**S**cooter Boy...**S**kin head... **S**uede head...**S**uggsey.....
P.S.
Uh God!

...**T**rojan...**U**nisex....
LOOK! Just want my hair **CUT**, right?
Nothing **PONCEY!!**

aAh!
Got an interview, have we?
Yeah... sort of, as it goes

I got to go and ask my parents for money....
I can't exist on my ****** grant...

An *Asking your Dad for Money* hair cut, eh?

You want... The ***Sir Keith Joseph Cut***... ..pun intended, of course! *Ho ho!*
Uh
Gawd!
Er..Dad...I'm ***skint*** now, and next year...on top of your parental contribution, d'you think you could..uh.. see your way...

Live-in Lover
B. RYAN
VETERINARIAN
SURGERY 4–6pm
MeeyoW!
This is poor Mr Tibbles... I think he needs some therapy...
Oh.... so what's the problem?
Well, lately... ever since my fiancé moved in with me, he's been a very naughty pussy!
Oh?
Yeah! He's really aggressive.. he BITES my fiancé! He CLAWS him... he just can't stand him!
You can say that again!
He's stopped utilizing the litter box.. he soils his cat duvet..!
He's never done that before! He's always been really sweet-natured! And he's SUCH a nice puddy-tat... .. I don't know why he's changed...
We've lived together SUCH a long time... haven't we, pussykins?
She's been my mistress for FIVE years, you know
Ever since I left college and lived on my own! He's such company!... Sometimes I think I owe my sanity to him!
FIVE years! Best years of my life, I've given her!
I had him as a kitten... he was a stray... .. I had him neutered and all that...... I think he's SAGGITARIUS....
For her, I gave up my freedom, my independence & my chances of fatherhood!
But right now, he's SCREWING UP my life and my relationship!! What do I do with him?
For 5 years I've been her faithful, live-in, domestic companion...
And now she's getting hitched to that wimp, Michael!!! ☆?**!
He's jealous of your fiancé, that's all...
Five years she's been my mistress!!
Poor Mr Tibbles! Look, he's almost human! Aaah... if he could talk, he would! Tell me what you want, Pussy....
Palimony!
© Posy Simmonds

Dovene de Lute
MOON FLUSH

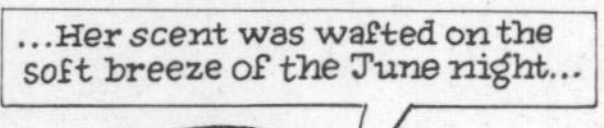

...Her scent was wafted on the soft breeze of the June night...

...Carlton exposed himself, by rearing out of the shadow of the catalpas, and moved towards her..... On this, their last meeting, how ashen was his face, how steely his grey eyes!
Stop that, Wilfred!
Stoppit!

How could he tell her it was all over? That their love was doomed? He looked at her moist lips, at the velvet column of her throat, at the twin globes that heaved under the bodice of her silken gown....
...Ah, one last kiss, and then...farewell!
Ooh! Your claws!
Stoppit!
What's got into you!?

...He clutched her to him, quite violently. With a moan, she
Tsk!
Now that's enough!
You're going OUT, Wilfred!

HIS SCENT WAS WAFTED ON THE SOFT BREEZE...
!

SALOME UNDULATED OUT OF THE SHADOW OF THE DUSTBINS...
HEY! GORGEOUS PERFUME!
WHAT IS IT?
O...JUST MY USUAL OLD SPRAY...EAU DE TOILETTE....

SUDDENLY, TO HIS DISMAY, SALOME ADOPTS THE LORDOSIS POSITION!
CRIKEY!
I SAY! STEADY THE BUFFS!

I'VE GOT TO TELL HER IT'S OVER! OUR LOVE IS DOOMED!

IT'S CHOKE! NO GOOD! IT'S ALL OVER BETWEEN US!
GASP WHAT!?

OUR LOVE IS DOOMED! IT CANNOT BE!
NO! NO!

TOMORROW! THEY'RE TAKING ME...TO THE VET'S! CHOKE YOU KNOW WHAT THAT MEANS...
ARRG!

DOCTORED!
NO! NO!

AND SO...ONE LAST KISS.....
Merooow!
Waroooo

OH GOD!
THOSE BLOODY CATS!!
THIRD TIME THIS WEEK!
Miaoooo

...ONE LAST KISS...
Warowooo
Meeowoo

...AND THEN...
WHUMP!

..FAREWELL!

...Never to see him again! She stood on the quay, waving, waving, till long after his sail had dipped beyond the horizon.... and wept as if her heart would break...

SNIFF
SNIFF

Flying Fur

In the Toy Department, besides *dolls* and *little plastic men*, covered in weaponry, there are lots & lots of *furry animals*....

... There are *teddies* and *pandas* and *woof-woofs* and *pussy cats*..

...*bunny-wunnies* and *chick-chicks* and *quack-quacks* and *goosey-ganders*....and *foxies* and *jumbos* and *oink-oinks*...

...*All* of whom, as representatives of the *Animal Kingdom*, are absolutely ***FED UP*** to the back teeth with the ***Human Race***.

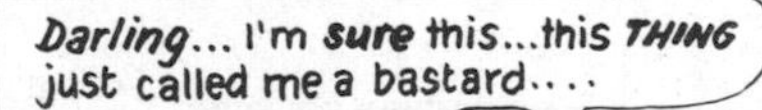

MAY DAY
What better way of spending the May Day holiday, than driving to the coast to visit my MOTHER at her Rest Home....
We try to go as often as we can....
...but it's a long, cross-country drive....
Mummee! Feel SICK again!
...and the children aren't the travellers they might be...
Come on! Can't wait here all day!
Better now, Manda?
TPD
ANGLO
CONTINENTAL
Feel SICK!
Oh God! Not AGAIN!
The traffic's always... ......none too clever.....
But it gives her such... pleasure, beforehand, to say we're coming...and, afterwards, to say we've been.....
Playing Scrabble, Mrs Weber?
No! George and family are coming
Poor, poor thing! Must be an AWFUL life..... T.V...Scrabble..comparing ailments...institutional food...none of her own furniture...oh dear... oh dear!
And she LOVES to see us.....for about twenty minutes.....
Well...I think I'd like to watch the RACING, now, dears.....
Right... we're here, kids...
We never come empty handed...

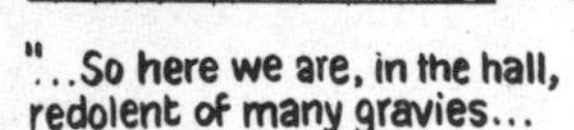
"...So here we are, in the hall, redolent of many gravies...

...110 miles on the clock.... stiff...travel-stained..... ...GUILTY....
You smell of SICK!
So do YOU!

...Here is the beaming Matron....
SUCH a pity you live so far away!

...Here is Mother.....
Hallo, strangers!

...Oh, I've read this one...never mind, Matron'll like it-She takes them to the hospital.... D'you think you should take the children to the beach soon?..I do like to watch Sport Grandstand at 3.00...Pity about PLAIN chocolates...I only ever offer MILK...Those poor flowers! Never last in the heating... I'll have to sit & watch them die...that's all I do, sit & watch things die... Wendy, dear, would you mind SWITCHING on...
MAYDAY! MAYDAY! MAYDAY!......

Turning an Honest Penny

Times have been tough in Tresoddit... ...for *Kevin Penwallet*, ex-lecturer in anthropology....

...Lean season has followed lean season... and, in the end, even the ideals of strong men, bow to the prevailing economic draught....

...and now, *Kevin Penwallet*, ex-purveyor of all that is **NATURAL**, has given over his shelves to **NATURE**....

For **NATURE** is *every-where!* All over the tea-towels & cosies & oven gloves & scatter cush-ions & mob-capped jars of preserves....

...*All over the sets of plates*...& little hand-bells & figurines, and even the *slate pictures*, which Kevin, against his better nature, creates himself...

And Kevin's *better nature does revolt!*

ME! ME of all people....!! Perpetuating the **MYTH!!** This **MYTH!** which excludes **TRUTH**... excludes any **REALITY**... of the **HARSHNESS** of **Nature** and **Country Life!**

Oh God Oh God!

But *how* can one deplore this peddling of Nature...with its whimsy...its sentiment, its bogus gentility...its nostalgia ...when the till rings all day...and two village girls have been given employment?

As he sits at the back of the shop, scratching a masted schooner upon slate, Kevin dreams of a way of righting the balance, regarding Nature & the country...of telling it like it is...

Announcing a most important porcelain plate collection.....

THE PENWALLET PLATES

The Haunting Beauty of our Coastline Heritage, recaptured in finest porcelain, by one of Europe's master craftsmen!

In his first series of collector's plates, the severely-gifted artist, ***Kevin Penwallet***, has set out to recreate all the intriguing magnificence of our ***Sea-Girt Isles***...hand-painted, in vivid, ceramic colours, upon exquisite, white porcelain.

The Collection portrays **12** dramatically different aspects of our spume-soaked shores... each plate a full *5¼*" in diameter ...to preserve all the remark-able detail, that is a hallmark of Penwallet's art.

Marvel at "**Oil-Drenched Gannet**"...every oily feather faultlessly exact, as it expires amongst the plastic flotsam of the shoreline!

Marvel again at "**Lonely Windsurfer**,"..the expression on the lad's face, as, gusted by a mischievous off-shore wind, he drifts far, far out to sea, beyond the reach of the Inshore Rescue Service!

Note the shimmering beauty of "**Hauling in the Catch**": A brace of boats lie at anchor, upon a limpid sea... In the foreground, burly **Customs Officers** haul in their day's catch of heroin, while the saucy smugglers dream of the years of enforced idle-ness that lie ahead!

Masterly beyond words, is Penwallet's "***Leisure Centre at Eventide***".....the lofty buildings straddling both sides of the once bosky peninsula. ....whilst "***Dog caught Short on Sandcastle***," places the artist in the ranks of the World's most Outstanding Animal Portraitists......and *who* could resist the sheer sen-timent of "***Old Village Post Office***," with its queue of re-dundant china-clay workers ...characters, all!

The Penwallet Plates will inevitably attract admiration from all those who *see* them on your wall... but this limited edition is available only to those collectors who enter their subscriptions before October 1st 1985... **£25** per plate.

The Penwallet Plates
Tresoddit CORNWALL
Yes! RUSH me my Penwallet collection of 12 distinctive, Porcelain plates
I enclose cheque for £ ________
Name ________________
Address ________________

Where there's a will....

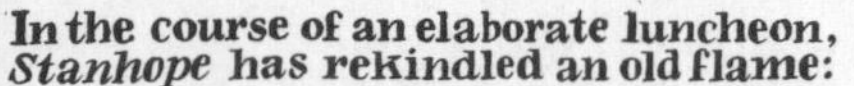
In the course of an elaborate luncheon, Stanhope has rekindled an old flame:

My place?
Oh dear...that's a tiny bit hors de combat this afternoon ....John's there...
Oh...
I see
Well.. perhaps some other time...eh?

Hang on...What about YOUR place?
O...that's a bit TRICKY...

But I thought you said...um...um your...um...wife'd gone ahead to the country for Easter..?
Er...yes..so I did...

...and the au pair's gone too...mm?
Yes...true... ...very true...

...so, there's NO ONE there! your house is QUITE, Quite ...EMPTY....mmm?
Erm...

..er...don't get me wrong... spirit is willing, and all that... ...it's just a bit...DIFFY.... ...One has to be very, very careful, these days.....

CAREFUL!?...you can't mean...? Really, Stanhope! Assure you, haven't got AIDS!

NO, no, no! Not THAT! No, no, no!..... ...I mean, of course, one has to consider it... ...but in your...our case...no, no...don't misunderstand me...
...It's just...one has to be, you know, ...CAREFUL.....

I don't know. What d'you mean? Herpes? Pudding Club?
No! Something much worse...

What?
Um...
...NEIGHBOURHOOD WATCH.....

..Our street...burglars' paradise... it's got a Neighbourhood Watch Scheme....
There's bloody Primula Stokes, opposite, with her binocs, logging every irregular coming and going in her Filofax...she takes polaroids of Jehovah's Witnesses, for Godsake...!

God, how impossible!.. absolutely bloody!
Well...there might be a way....

...Listen, we go in my car...we park round the corner, in Mitre Street...now, you ring Primula Stokes on the car phone...while she goes to answer it, I make a break for it, and get in the house, leaving the door on the latch.....
Now, you hang up, when she answers...and that gives you 30 seconds to zip like greased whatsit into my house, before she can get back upstairs to her vantage point...she smokes a lot, so she's not too nippy on her feet.....

...we repeat the process on leaving...
Remember, we won't be able to draw the curtains..
We'd have to use Willy's room -that's not overlooked...
Well...
...perhaps some other time, Stanhope....

The Webers and friends from France pause after visiting the *Royal Academy*...
(BRITISH ART in the Twentieth Century)

Consequences

The driver of an expensive car....

...was stopped by a policeman.........
Yes, officer, what can I do for you?

...... He said to him.....
Excuse me, sir... Sorry to trouble you... but you do not appear to be displaying a TAX DISC....

.....He said to him.....
Oh I'm FRIGHTFULLY sorry, Sergeant!
Constable, actually, sir
Constable! My new disc arrived in the post this morning... CLEAN forgot to put it on!
..The old one.... whole shooting-match dropped orf the windscreen...
Then my children were playing with it... lorst it... and, really, I...I..
Awfully careless, I AM sorry!

...and the consequence was:
Yeah, well... that's all right, sir..
Make sure you put your new one on, when you get home, mind...
Absolutely! Will do!
Right, mind how you go, then....

The owner of an expensive car....

...was addressed by a policeman....
Excuse me....

....He said to her...
You realise you could be causing an obstruction, waiting here, don't you?
Your husband's car, is it?

...She said to him....
No, I'm not married
Borrowed the boyfriend's car, eh?
No, it's my car...
May I see your licence, please?
...and the consequence was:
Yes, well that seems to be in order... all right? Mind how you go, then...

The owner of an expensive car.....
uh oh!
...saw that he was about to be stopped by a policeman...

...who was about to say to him......
Fancy car... where did you nick this, then, eh?
It's MY car!
A likely story!

He said to himself....
I'm NOT driving in there! I HATE Consequences!
.....and drove straight off to another page...
Oi!
Hey! You can't just drive off! That's not playing the game!

..Leaving the World to say.....
If you drive a motor car...
You'll get stopped, the chances are.
But as a rule, you'll be all right,
If you're male and posh and white.

Bless my soul! Half three! Time to get back to the grindstone!

Gordon Bennet! Traffic Warden at my motor!

Or was it your Respect for Authority?
Oh..
....Consternoon, Afterble!
Just moving it!
Just moving it!

A Kind of Liberation

In the lunch-break, George Weber and a colleague nip out... each to do his shopping....
37 BATES
APPLES
What's the matter, George? Have I upset you?
George?

Have I upset you? I have... haven't I?
NO!

Well.... as a...um matter of fact... ...YES... you have...

37
Um... your behaviour in there... in the green-grocer's...
Oh! You mean I CAMPED it up a bit?
Yes!

Yes... well, I did... I admit I did..... I am GAY, after all....

I know you are!

Oh, but for Heaven's sake, don't THINK for a minute that's why I...er... No, no, NO! .... It's just..er...that you don't usually ...er....

...Behave like a raving queen...?
No...I don't, usually....
...But that bloke in there...he got right up my nose!

Him... going ON and ON about us doing the shopping for our lucky WIVES.... got right on my wick.... EVERYWHERE the assumption that EVERYONE is HETEROSEXUAL!!

I CAN'T STAND being treated like a HOUSE-HUSBAND!

That's all very well...but what about ME, now!?
You're all right..you ARE a kind of house-husband!

YES! Years I've been going in that shop... he's OK, that bloke...., I mean, for a long time, he used to TEASE me... about why it was always ME that did the shopping & cooking for the family... He thought: REAL MEN DON'T DO THE SHOPPING... REAL MEN DON'T DO HOUSE-WORK... REAL MEN DON'T make vichyssoise...

...But since then, we've had quite a few CHATS... you know, about the changing rôles of men & women... and he's just come round to the idea that it's NORMAL to share domestic work — it's not unmanly to do the shopping etc... you know: the whole TOUGH/TENDER conflation....

And then YOU go in there and do your number...
..and now I'm afraid he may be back where I started....

I told him... REAL MEN don't do the shopping...

George Weber has suddenly been asked to write a reference for a job for one of his former students:

TO WHOM IT MAY CONCERN:

SIMON CUTLAS

As Simon Cutlas's Liberal Studies tutor over a period of three years, I can speak as someone who knew his work in his main subject, chiefly by report, and can speak only of his character, attitude and results in courses he followed in this department.

he followed in this department.

I am sorry to say that his attendance can only be described as poor and sporadic. He was rarely on time for lectures, seminars or tutorials and his contributions to both of the latter were unintelligent and tangential...

His was a bad influence on fellow students, his relations with them less than cordial: his manner alternating between a sullen, speechless affectation of superiority, and sudden aggressive volubility.

I cannot describe him as someone who used his time at the Polytechnic in a positive and constructive way, or that his attitude and industry suggest that he would be of the slightest use in the post, such as outlined in your job description. I have always found him impatient, selfish and wooden.

eorge Weber
enior Lecturer, Liberal Studies

he followed in this department.

I am glad to say that his attendance can't be described as poor and sporadic. He was on time for lectures, seminars or tutorials and his contributions to both of the latter were intelligent and tangential. amusingly

His was an influence on fellow students, his relations with them ~~less than~~ cordial: his manner alternating between a subtle speech and sudden amusing volubility.

I can describe him as someone who used his time at the Polytechnic in a positive and constructive way, & that his attitude and industry suggest that he would be of the utmost use in the post, such as outlined in your job description. I have always found him patient, un selfish and solid oak.

George Weber
Senior Lecturer, Liberal Studies

In a large bookshop, best-selling author, J.D. Crouch is signing copies of the second volume of his trilogy of social historical novels, *"The Harlow Years"*.....
("...Provocative in its attempt at a panoptic vision..." T.L.S.)

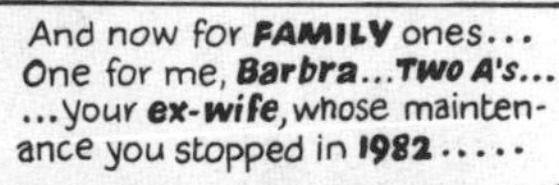

One for your children, Rachel & Toby, who you never bother to see, but about whom you talk so fondly in interviews.....

the pleasure of their company
The Directors of Walmer & Wilcox Ltd invite you to celebrate the publication of "UP BARDFIELD" by J.D. CROUCH
on Tuesday, February 17th 1987 at 69 Breeveley St LONDON W1 6·30 - 8·30
R.S.V.P
Bell
09 Ex 206

God, YOU here, too!?
Yeah-h...dunno WHY I come to these things! ...HATE them! Can't stand other authors....
Nooo... dunno why WE'RE here, either... can't stand parties like this.... rectal ache department.......

Just SO BORING! Complete, pointless timewaste....lot of clapped-out, free-loading old f*rts... I mean, what's it all FOR!?
Tsk.. Could've been watching "East Enders"!...

Dunno WHY I come to these things
And look at old Crouch..
Boring old....
Still miffed at not getting the Booker...
Oooh is he?

Said 'hallo' to little Vernon? ...you know he's leaving?
What! IS he?!
LEAVING!?
Yes..going to Harrier Press...art director..
Don't know if I'm glad or sorry...never liked all that silver lettering he shoves on my books...

Who's the one in the daft hat?
Julia Benbow ...she's the new publicity...
O, is that what she looks like!
Yeah, you want to watch it.... She's like THAT with old Max!
Ooh!

Look! Look!
See what I see...thought those two weren't on speakers!
You KNOW what Binns called him last week in Book Review...."Less than compulsive reading"!.... You know, he really went for the gonads!

Watch out, Nick...your foe, B. Nuttley...coming this way
That's OK...I love being polite to vicious critics

Tough on old Lumsden, isn't it.? his last book being remaindered..
WAS it!?
That why he's got legless?

Yeah, well I'm surprised to see her here!
I mean, I heard she's doing the next one with Kernel Books..... ...cos' Kernel don't bother with royalties...they just whack a huge flat fee upfront...like 25K
Really!?
Must tell my agent

Well, I suppose we'll see you next week at Celia's launch...?
You MIGHT...but I so HATE these dos, I just don't know WHY we come to them....
Nor do I

Smoke Signals
It's Guy Fawkes.... that night of communal celebration..... But, sad to tell, in these back gardens, it is only the smoke that mingles in the November air....
The Belpers' Smoke
The Timmis' Smoke
The Webers' Smoke
The Belpers take exception to the Timmis and the Weber bonfires:
The TIMMISES! Absolute bloody DISGRACE!! It's CHEMICAL POLLUTION!
God!
One whiff of THAT!
As for the WEBERS! 'Struth! Obscene, burning those! And him a TEACHER!
They could've RE-CYCLED them....
Given them to the OLD PEOPLE'S HOME...
The Timmises think the Belpers and the Webers deserve a rocket....
Oh, I say! The BELPERS! Fancy burning soiled things like that..! DISGUSTING!
Those bloody WEBERS! Culture snobs!
Burning all your dirty, lefty ones, are you!?
And the Webers find the Timmis and Belper bonfires absolutely beyond the pale.....
BELPERS! Bringing the countryside back, to BURN it! Thoroughly SELFISH!
Tsk!
Yes.. them and their HOLISTIC bonfire!
As for the TIMMISES! Victims of Colour Supplement Culture!
Bring out the OLD & burn it.. Go and buy the NEW!
I dunno why they're making so much fuss about ours!
OUR bonfire's absolutely ORGANIC... only WOOD and natural stuff, we've brought back from the cottage...
Yes.. there ARE one or two of Daisy's disposable nappies on here... but they're CELLULOSE, for Godsake! You can't give them to the DUSTMEN..
Dunno why they're getting their knickers in a twist about our bonfire...
It's only our old foam'n'plastic settee ...bit of nylon SHAG PILE out of the rumpus room. few cushions ...that's all...
Really don't see why they're being so stupid about ours...
Only burning a few old books.. ..who wants early issues of IKON? ...set of Roger Martin du Gard? ... bound copies of old C.N.A.A.* documents?... So much intellectual lumber....
.. offerings to Vulcan...
..out of the ashes... forging some phoenix? .... mm
* Council for National Academic Awards

Only Connect

O, what a marvellous sight! Look at that!
Oooh, Wendy! I SAY!!!
Yummy Yum!

English Spring lamb! ... What an absolutely beautiful leg!
Well, it cost a leg... and an arm! But it's all meat...not much bone...
Ooh, dem bones! Oh dem bones!

Sorry?...What was that? Did you say something, Pippa?
No...?

Funny... I distinctly heard someone say.....
Ooo... dem bones!
Golly!
!

..ooo...de leg bone's connected to de thigh-bone...!

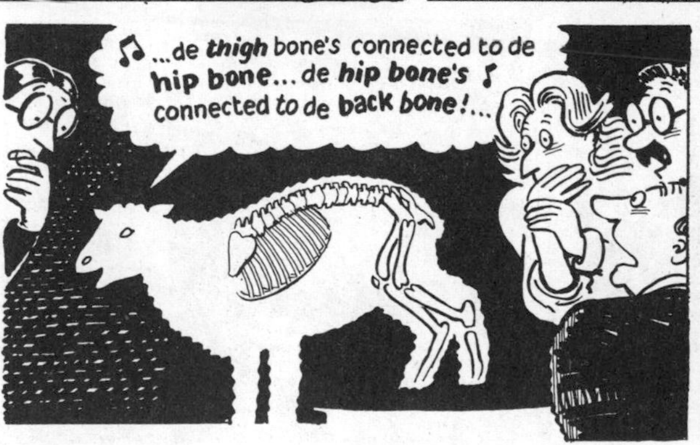
...de thigh bone's connected to de hip bone... de hip bone's connected to de back bone!...

Oh hear de name of the Lord!

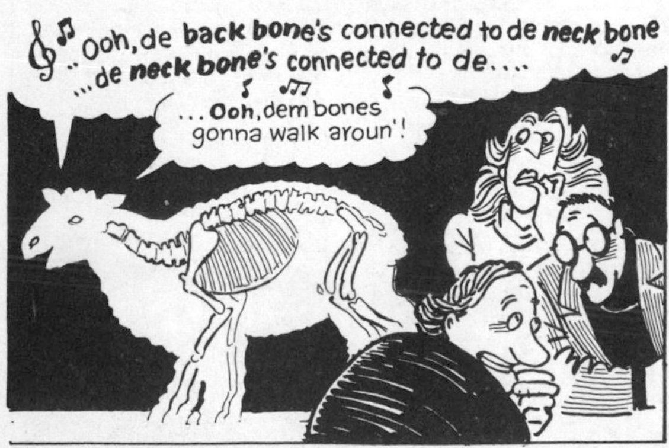
..ooh, de back bone's connected to de neck bone ...de neck bone's connected to de....
...Ooh, dem bones gonna walk aroun'!

Shut up! Shut up! You're putting us right off our lunch!
Really?

Sorry!

Course, we don't eat much red meat, these days...
...it's when you see them skipping about in the fields isn't it...?
I don't miss it, like I'd miss chicken...
...see, one never thinks of joints as animals, does one?

Cutting the cord

George Weber is having a vexatious time with his eldest daughter....
The little..!
She has! She's gone and propositioned him!
GERK! Who?

Belinda and Stanhope, that's who...
Ooh... bit of an Oh Christ situation, eh?
I'll say!

Randy old sod, Stanhope... ...flash as a rat with a gold tooth! HAR Haaaa!

Tsk! Calls himself a friend... I'm not having HIM and my daughter....
But, what would your fiancé say!

Oh, do say YES...
O, darling, you know how I adore you!
....I mean... I remember you in your carry-cot....

Believe me, I'm very, very touched and flattered.... much as I'd love to... but What would your Dad say?
Nothing to do with him, now!

He refused to do it! He said: he didn't own me.... I wasn't his property... I'm a free agent...
Even so, I might feel a tiny bit terrible...

YOU might feel a tiny bit terrible!?... What about ME?!!
I'm not having HER and YOU...
Shuddup, Dad!
It's none of your business, now!

You said you didn't OWN me!... You said I'm not your property! You said you'd rather die than hand me over like a chattel! You said you'd feel a berk in a penguin suit..!

...That's why I've every right to ask Stanhope to give me away at my wedding.....
..and if he won't do it, I'll ask Edmund!

YOU'd give me away, Edmund, wouldn't you?
Anything you shay, shweetheart!

You're bloody NOT, Edmund!!! ...or YOU, Stanhope!...look, she's MY daughter, not YOURS!
Too late, Dad

Wait!...look! I do appreciate the need for some sort of ritual..er.. behaviour on my part....an exogamous paradigm... um...
I agree to ACCOMPANY you up the aisle..O.K?...as your equal...
Yeah?

But, do you, Dad, promise to hire a suit and to cut the cr*p, as long as the service lasts?
Speak now...or forever hold your codpiece!

Photographs taken by Barry Parry....
(Alliance)

...at the wedding of Miss Belinda Weber,
(Conservative)

...eldest daughter of Mr and Mrs George Weber,....
(Staunch Labour) *(Green Party)*

...and Mr Alistair Razer-Dorke,
(Conservative)

...son of Lt Col and Mrs Desmond Razer-Dorke.
(Deep-dyed Conservative)

GENERAL BREAKDOWN OF WEDDING PARTY:

Con.
Lab.
All.

Mr Edmund Heep.
(Spoiled ballot paper)

Mr Stanhope Wright *(ex fair-weather Labour, Soi-disant S.D.P / closet Conservative)*, sharing a joke with Mr Edmund Heep.

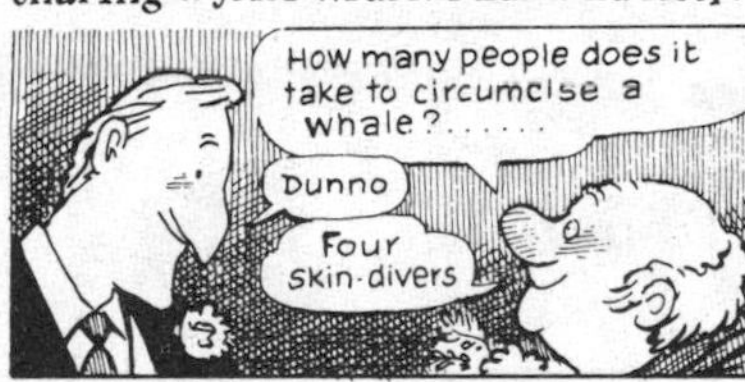

Mr Julian Heep (Red Caucus)
Mr Jolyon Heep (Conservative)

Mr Kevin Penwallet
(Mebyon Kernow)

Mrs Brinsley Bowe *(Con)* & her daughter, Penny *(Lab)*

Mrs Stanhope Wright *(Tactical Voter)* and Miss Jocasta Wright (Don't Know, Don't Care).

Benji and Sophie Weber *(Alliance)*

Mr Edmund Heep reading the telemessages.

It says: Please send photo of couple.....
...not MOUNTED...just holding hands!
Harhaar Haa!

PICTURES through the AGES
FAITHFUL FRIEND
May
PETER RABBIT
LUKE
PETER RABBIT
Remember
Sophie Tues. Karate
Ballet 3.30
Tim DENTIST 4.00
PTA
Cleaning
Cheese
Rabbit food
media schedules:
90 Day Shape-up Plan:
TaB
© Posy Simmonds

The World turned Upside-down
Hallo, Ronnie! Ooh, we're looking GORGEOUS, as per usual! Haaa!
O, hallo, Miss Pye...
Oh B*gg*r*tion! Mrs Truscott - gone out to lunch, has she, dear?
Ur... Yes... ten minutes ago...
O, be a good boy... just run over the road and give her this, would you, dear? She's in the George...
Yes, Miss Pye..
Oh...and get me twenty Bensons, there's a pet...
LIFT
Only room for a little 'un!
In you come, dear!
LIFT
'Allo, darlin'
Cheer up!
RECEPTION
Smile!
It may never happen!
Not bad...
Hello, Ballsy!
GEORGE IV
Fancy a gargle, Doris?
Yeah, don't mind if I do
ALES
Ooh, make way for the little gentleman, Denise!
O, sorry, dear!
Pint of 4 star, please, Rocky
Mrs Truscott... Miss Pye said to give you this...
O, the sales figures! Oh, Ronnie! You ANGEL!
Ooh! This nice, young gentleman work for you, Erica?
Wouldn't kick that out of bed, would you, Mandy?
Well, dunno
Hallo, Lizzy... ooh, we're looking gorgeous, as per usual!
Go and get us 20 Bensons, would you, pet..?

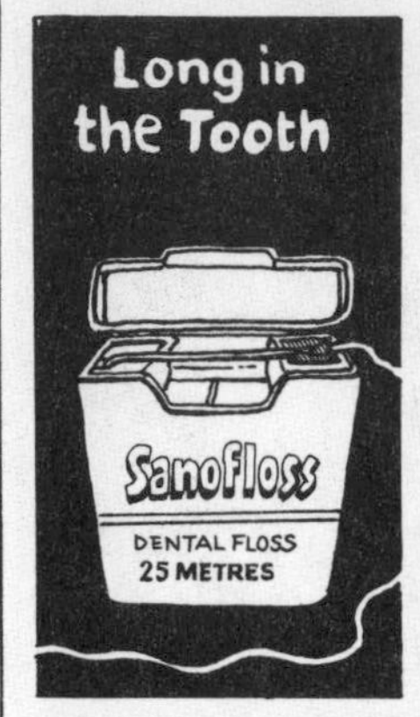
Long in the Tooth
SanoFloss
DENTAL FLOSS
25 METRES

Tic!

Tic!

Toc!

Tic!

K-r-r-r-t!

Tic!
Toc!

Tic!
Toc!

Tic!
Toc!

Stanhope...
Tic!

mm?

We must have another baby... before it's too late......
EH!?

This is a bit sudden...! What's brought all this on?

I dunno...
Tic!

...it's just I have this feeling of TIME running out....
Really..?
Tic
Toc
Tic

At this mellow season of the year.....
...when all hearts o'erflow with love...
...and the Festive Board groans with Choice viands.........
....and a ruddy glow suffuses each familiar face......
...we raise a glass to all those Dear & Near....
Toast-wise, I'd like to...
...those far-flung friends, those wayfaring ones....
...All Those who are not here to share this Tinselled Day!
...I'd like us to drink to.....
Rin-g!
Rin-ng!
Hallo..
God! Martha, not now! I can't speak!!
I know you only wanted to wish me a happy... yeah! I know that!
Listen, I must GO... I can't... I KNOW it's tough on you! ...and you're all alone.... I KNOW!! It's TERRIBLE!
So, how d'you think it is for ME...? walled up all holiday with them!
Hey! don't lay that on me! Martha! MARTHA?..... Listen, I'll make it up to you, sugar... I will!
OK? ..now I must GO... What?... Do I wish you were doing WHAT with me? THAT!? Well...
Sound more enthusiastic? For CHRISSAKE, Martha ...remember where I AM!!
Course I do! I DO! OK, OK... I·LOVE·YOU.. OK? Yes, call me at the office... Look I must... yes... G'Bye....
PHEW
ABSENT FRIENDS!
Absent Friends...
© Posy Simmonds

It's not even midnight when Stanhope returns from the office Christmas bash.....

Good Sports

In the games at Katie's birthday party, there are NO *winners* and NO *losers*......
♪ Get into the groove girl...you gotta give your love to m

I'm the WINNER
AGAIN!

Right, now...
Tamsin's the last one in...so she gets to give everyone a prize...
I'm the winner!
Divonac

Hey, I got a Snowman pad and pencil!
But I was the winner...
Divonac

You see, the *important* thing in *games* is NOT to *win*...but to *take part*....
Oh, I so agree!
Well, I think it's a good idea... NO declared winners....

I mean, it's what they do at Rachel's school, now...you know, non-competitive games & sports...
Right...now is everybody a sleeping lion?
You're not, Benji!

...the children just play co-operatively... ...just enjoy the game for itself....
And YOU, Fanny! Out you go!

Much fairer at parties...cos' you always get one or two kids, who NEVER win anything!
Oh, MORTIFYING for them! ....Terrible boo-hoos, all the way home!

Doesn't matter, darling! Not everyone can win! Not the end of the world...you got a going home present..
Booo Hooo!
And I won a My Little Pony money box!

Oh God, I mean, I remember children's parties!...Just HELL ON EARTH! I was always out First go...I never won!
Out goes Lucy! ..And it's Tamsin left! The only sleepy Leo the Lion...
Well! Well!

...The HUMILIATION of always losing! It's so damaging for the kids' self-image....they learn to think of themselves as losers....
So Tamsin gets to give out the going-home presents....O.K?

This way, everyone gets a present....
And everyone's happy!
Ah yes!
Look!
Mum! Look what I got!

Oh, Tamsin! Come on, cheer up! You've got exactly the same amount of presents as they have! Everyone got the same...
Bud dey didernt WIN dem! BOO HOO! I was the WINNER!
BOO HOOOO!

Edmund Heep's Problem Page
Spot the Difference
Can you spot 12 differences between these two genial scenes?
Merry Christmas!
Merry Chrishmas!
CRIPPO
CRIPPO
Spot the Rozzers
Can you find 4 constables in this picture?
Riddle-me-ree
Offisher, tell me, pray WHAT is brown and rings?
I do not know
Answer: DUNG-G!
What is the difference between a mad Dutchman and a drain-pipe?
..er...
One's a silly Hollander, the other's a hollow cylinder.
What is hard & pink in the mornings?
..erm...
The Financial Times crossword
Sjhowme therwaytergo Home!
Hic!
© Posy Simmonds